Year 5/Primary P6

NHAMMETT

Including
Lower-
achievers
in the
Maths
Lesson

Caroline Clissold
Sue Atkinson

HOPSCOTCH
EDUCATIONAL PUBLISHING

Contents

Published by
Hopscotch Educational Publishing Ltd,
29 Waterloo Place,
Leamington Spa CV32 5LA
Tel: 01926 744227

© 2001 Hopscotch Educational Publishing

Written by Caroline Clissold and Sue Atkinson
Series design by Blade Communications
Illustrated by The Drawing Room
Printed by Clintplan, Southam

ISBN 1-902239-59-8

Caroline Clissold and Sue Atkinson hereby assert their moral right to be identified as the authors of this work in accordance with the Copyright, Designs and Patents Act, 1988.

The authors would like to thank the many teachers and children from the following schools who trialled these activities:

Upton House School, Windsor, Berskshire

Benyon Primary School, South Ockendon, Essex

St. Joseph's RC Primary School, Stanford le Hope, Essex

West Thurrock Primary School, Thurrock, Essex

Christ Church C of E Primary School, South Croydon

Haymerle Special School, London

Bishop Perrin School, Richmond

Sheen Mount Primary School, Richmond

Summerbee Junior School, Bournemouth, Dorset

St Ives First School, St Ives, Ringwood, Hampshire

Mudeford Junior School, Christchurch, Dorset

Linwood School (Special), Bournemouth, Dorset

INSTANT ANSWER NUMBER MATRIX

×	1	2	3	4	5	6	7	8	9	10
0	0	0	0	0	0	0	0	0	0	0
1	1	2	3	4	5	6	7	8	9	10
2	2	4	6	8	10	12	14	16	18	20
3	3	6	9	12	15	18	21	24	27	30
4	4	8	12	16	20	24	28	32	36	40
5	5	10	15	20	25	30	35	40	45	50
6	6	12	18	24	30	36	42	48	54	60
7	7	14	21	28	35	42	49	56	63	70
8	8	16	24	32	40	48	56	64	72	80
9	9	18	27	36	45	54	63	72	81	90
10	10	20	30	40	50	60	70	80	90	100
11	11	22	33	44	55	66	77	88	99	110
12	12	24	36	48	60	72	84	96	108	120

×	11	12	13	14	15	16	17	18	19	20
0	0	0	0	0	0	0	0	0	0	0
1	11	12	13	14	15	16	17	18	19	20
2	22	24	26	28	30	32	34	36	38	40
3	33	36	39	42	45	48	51	54	57	60
4	44	48	52	56	60	64	68	72	76	80
5	55	60	65	70	75	80	85	90	95	100
6	66	72	78	84	90	96	102	108	114	120
7	77	84	91	98	105	112	119	126	133	140
8	88	96	104	112	120	128	136	144	152	160
9	99	108	117	126	135	144	153	162	171	180
10	110	120	130	140	150	160	170	180	190	200
11	121	132	143	154	165	176	187	198	209	220
12	132	144	156	168	180					

In the section on Inclusion, The National Curriculum states that schools have a responsibility to provide a broad and balanced curriculum for all pupils. It sets out three principles that are essential to developing a more inclusive curriculum:

A: Setting suitable learning challenges

B: Responding to pupils' diverse learning needs

C: Overcoming potential barriers to learning and assessment…

Including Lower-achievers in the Maths Lesson is a series of books that gives support for including in the daily maths lesson those children in the class who, for whatever reason, are struggling and therefore often failing.

The books can be used alongside the *Developing Numeracy Skills* books also published by Hopscotch Educational Publishing Ltd. You will find a cross-reference to these books on the chart on page 5.

CHAPTER CONTENT

The overall learning objectives

Each chapter has overall learning objectives that are based on the number key objectives in the *National Numeracy Strategy Framework for Teaching.*

The grid on page 5 shows where these key objectives are covered within the chapters in this book. The lessons in this Year 5/P6 book are based on the Number Key Objectives for Years 3–5 (P4–6) to be found in the *Framework for Teaching.*

The assessment focus

Each chapter is divided into 'sessions' – a set of activities that might last for one or more days. The assessment focus for each session is based on the key objectives and broken down into competencies that the children are expected to achieve within those key objectives.

An assessment chart can be found on pages 111 and 112.

With the whole class

This section includes activities that are suitable for everyone in the class but they focus on the work for the lower-achievers that follows. Therefore they use easy numbers so that the lower-achievers can cope with the maths concept being taught.

You can repeat the whole-class starter(s) over several days or choose another starter that focuses on a similar learning objective.

Some suggested vocabulary is given, but you should teach with your *National Numeracy Strategy Mathematical Vocabulary* to hand.

With the lower-achievers

These are activities that follow on from the whole-class starter and you can use them:

- in the middle of the lesson for children who are under-achieving

- during the next week or two to consolidate the concepts

- when you come back to that topic next term.

Within this section is a selection of activities, some to be done with adult guidance and some which can be done by selected children independently.

With adult support

Many of the activities require equipment. We use equipment so that we are developing the children's mental images and things such as number lines, 100 squares and cubes are absolutely crucial. Many of the activities are games as these can motivate and keep the children involved. You will need to train your children to play games if they are not used to them.

Once taught, some of these activities can be teacher-independent. Often there are examples of questions and other things to say to the children so that their vocabulary is extended.

In addition to the adult support during the activities, try to plan for times when an adult can give a few minutes 'catch up' time to a group of children at odd moments during the day, for example five minutes at the end of assembly or at the start or end of the day. (If possible, take children from more than one class for 'catch up' times to make the best use of an adult helper.)

Teacher-independent activities

These activities are suitable for lower-achievers to do on their own, depending how well they work independently. Again, many of them will require the use of maths equipment.

Plenary session

In this section a few questions are included to help lower-achievers reflect on their work, and sometimes there is an additional activity. Many of the whole-class starters can also be used as activities here.

Keep plenary sessions varied and interesting. They are times to sort out misconceptions, and times to generalise about what has been done. They are not just 'show and tell' times!

The photocopiable resource sheets

Some of the activities suggested in the teachers' notes require the use of resource sheets. A minimum of words is used on these, so helpers will need to have instructions on what to ask the children to do on them. Many of the sheets are blanks, requiring the teacher or adult to write in tasks at a suitable level of attainment.

On the sheets there is a space at the bottom that contains notes for the adult. Sometimes this space is blank. This has been done deliberately as the teacher or adult may wish to add a few notes for another adult to use with a specific child or group. Likewise the sheets may be sent home to the parents/carers and this space can be used for instructions to them.

Some of the artwork on the resource sheets is on the same theme as the *Developing Numeracy Skills* books. However, some of it is more varied to provide interest for the children. We have also provided 'clip art' sheets at the end of the resource sheet section, so that you can cut and stick pictures onto the children's sheets in order to change the appearance of the sheets when you want to use them more than once. This gives the sheets new life and gives the children plenty of practice to consolidate.

A general point about using the sheets with lower-achievers

Although the resource sheets provided in this book can be used several times, remember that it isn't recording maths that is important; it is whether the child can understand the concept. So use the sheets only when they are needed, such as for a teacher-independent activity or for assessment.

Spinners

Some of the games in the book need a spinner that works by trapping a paper-clip in the middle of the spinner then flicking the paper-clip round with a finger. Spinners are quieter than dice and give more choice.

Number lines

Have a large wall number line and 100 square up in each class. Remember that 100 squares are suitable for looking at patterns, such as for 10s, but are not ideal to do calculations on because children tend to get lost as they move from the end of one line to the start of the next. Number lines are much easier to use for calculations.

And finally, remember

We want children to feel positive and to feel that they are achieving well in maths. Working endlessly on activity sheets can be boring, and could even make a child feel they are failing. Use games where possible to reinforce concepts and skills. Be generous with praise.

This grid is made up of the key objectives for Years 4 and 5 plus other crucial learning, and shows the chapter(s) where these objectives are covered in this book. The grid also shows where the same area of learning can be found in the *Developing Numeracy Skills* series.

KEY OBJECTIVES	CHAPTERS	DNS – BOOK/CHAPTER
Round any positive integer less than 1000 to the nearest 10 or 100.	3	Year 5 – Chapter 3
Recognise simple fractions that are several parts of a whole, and mixed numbers. Recognise the equivalence of simple fractions.	9	Year 5 – Chapter 9
Use known number facts and place value to add or subtract mentally, including any pair of two-digit whole numbers.	4	Year 5 – Chapter 4
Know by heart facts for 2, 3, 4, 5 and 10 times tables.	6, 7	Year 5 – Chapter 6
Derive quickly division facts corresponding to the 2, 3, 4, 5 and 10 times tables.	6	Year 5 – Chapter 6
Find remainders after division.	8	Year 5 – Chapter 8
Choose and use appropriate number operations and ways of calculating (mental, mental with jottings, pencil and paper) to solve problems.	3, 4, 5, 6, 7, 8	Year 5 – Chapters 3, 4, 5, 6, 7, 8
Multiply and divide any positive integer up to 10,000 by 10 or 100 and understand the effect.	6	Year 5 – Chapter 6
Order a given set of positive and negative integers.	2	Year 5 – Chapter 2
Use decimal notation for tenths and hundredths.	10	Year 5 – Chapter 10
Round a number with one or two decimal places to the nearest integer.	2	Year 5 – Chapter 2
Relate fractions to division and to their decimal representations.	9, 10	Year 5 – Chapters 9, 10
Calculate mentally a difference such as 8006 – 2993.	4, 5	Year 5 – Chapters 4, 5
Know by heart all multiplication facts up to 10 x 10.	6, 7	Year 5 – Chapters 6, 7
Carry out short multiplication and division of a three-digit by a single-digit integer.	7	Year 5 – Chapter 7
Carry out long multiplication of a two-digit by a two-digit integer.	7	Year 5 – Chapter 7
Use all four operations to solve simple word problems involving numbers and quantities, including time, explaining methods and reasoning.	4, 5, 6, 7, 8, 9	Year 5 – Chapters 4, 5, 6, 7, 8, 9

Place value

Overall learning objectives

■ Read and write whole numbers up to seven digits.

■ Know what each digit in a number represents and partition into thousands, hundreds, tens and units.

■ Multiply and divide any whole number by 10.

Key words

greater than

equal to

divisibility

Big numbers

Assessment focus

■ Can the children read large numbers accurately?

■ Do the children know what each digit in a number represents?

Resources

■ Resource sheets 1, 2, 3, 4 and 5
■ counters
■ digit cards
■ place value cards

With the whole class

■ Explain to the children that today they will be learning how to make and read large numbers. Using digit cards, they should make up the numbers you call out. For example, *"Put the two digit cards that read 25 in front of you. Now make that read 425."* *"Now change these digits around to make the highest number you can. What number is it?"* (542) Ask someone to come to the board and write up which number the 5 represents (500). Then continue along these lines: *"Now make your number read 6542. Now swap the 5 and the 4. What is the new number?"* (6452) *"Swap the 6 and the 2; what is the new number?"* (2456) *"Jasmine, come and write the number that the 5 represents. Now the 6,"* and so on.

■ Continue building the number up until you reach millions, swapping numbers around, asking the children what the new number is and inviting them to write numbers on the board. Make sure that you target the lower-achievers with the numbers they can read. Can they find the numbers they need to swap and place them in the correct positions?

With the lower-achievers

With adult support

Choose from:

1   You will need a teaching set of place value cards, choosing up to three different thousands, hundreds, tens and units numbers. The children need to have their own set of place value cards which are the same as yours, so that they can model what you are doing. Make a number, such as 539. Ask the children to copy what you have done. Ask someone to tell everyone which three numbers make up 539. Check the answer by separating the cards 500, 30 and 9. Put them back together again, making sure that they follow you and understand. Repeat this, working up to thousands numbers, such as 6812. Ask them to write down what the 8 is (800), the 6 (6000) and so on. Separate the cards to check their answers.

2   Using place value cards again, build up four H, T, U numbers, for example 683, 997, 294 and 187. Choose some children to write them on the board. Discuss which is the largest and why. Put them in order. Aim towards the children thinking that they need to look at the most significant digit first to put them in order. Ask them to write down what the 6 represents (600). Do the same with the 9 (900), 2 (200) and 1 (100). Repeat this activity but use numbers that have the same hundreds digit, for example 453, 439, 424 and 486. This will encourage the children to look at the tens digit.

Teacher-independent activities

Choose from:

1   Give the children copies of Resource sheet 1. They should first make the numbers on the sheet using their place value cards, then separate

them and record the numbers that are put together to make the original number.

Number	Hundreds	Tens	Units
345	300	40	5

2   Resource sheet 2 is similar to Resource sheet 1, but is for working on thousands numbers and for the children to make their own numbers to partition.

3   Using Resource sheet 3 and some counters, ask the children to put a counter on each row of the chart and write down the whole number. For example, if counters are put on 2000, 500, 40 and 9 they write down 2549.

4   Resource sheet 4 should be used as a place value game for two players. The children will need their digit cards, face down in front of them. Player 1 picks a card and puts that number in their grid in either the H, T or U position. Player 2 does the same. They do this three times in total. The object of the game is to make the highest number.

Player 1 picks 5 (T), then   Player 2 picks 8 (H), then
1 (U) and then 4 (H).   1 (U) and then 1 (T).

H	T	U
4	5	1

H	T	U
8	1	1

In the above example, Player 2 wins the game.

Plenary session

■   Divide the class into two teams. Draw two thousands, hundreds, tens and units grids on the board.

Thousands	Hundreds	Tens	Units

Each team picks at random a digit card and decides in which column to place it. Appoint a child as the 'picker' or the one who fills in the grid. The winning team is the one who makes the highest number.

■   *"What did you learn today about numbers?"*

■   *"Which part of the lesson did you enjoy most?"*

■   Play 'Bingo'. The children will need a copy of the grid (Resource sheet 5), or they could draw their own. Ask them to fill it in with numbers. The lower-achievers could use numbers up to thousands, or whatever they can manage. You call out a number ending in a zero, for example 600, 3000 or 50, and anyone who has that number anywhere in any of their chosen numbers should cross it out. The winner is the first child to cross all their numbers out.

2378	356	254	1546
5436	7658	698	4657
2908	4765	354	1488

So, if you call out *"600"*, the following numbers will be crossed out – 7658, 698 and 4657. If you call out *"50"*, the following numbers will be crossed out – 356, 254, 7658, 4657 and 354, and so on.

10 times bigger (and smaller)

Assessment focus

- Can the children multiply and divide by 10?

Resources

- digit cards
- large digits on A4 paper
- Resource sheets 6 and 7
- string and three Multilink or Unifix cubes
- an abacus

With the whole class

- Tell the children that today they will be thinking about how much they know about multiplying and dividing by 10. Ask them what they already know about multiplying by 10. Say that together you are going to make a number 10 times bigger.

- Write a large Th, H, T and U high up on the board. Invite a child (preferably a lower-achiever) to stand below the U with a large digit, such as 8. Say that if you multiply that number by 10, it becomes 10 times bigger.

- Now invite another child to hold a 0 and 'bump' the first child along one place to stand under the T, while they stand below the U. Repeat this several times using different children and gradually making the starting number bigger, for example 30 000. Make sure that the children realise that when you multiply by 10, the digits move one place to the left. Don't tell them to *"add a nought."* Extend this to decimal numbers.

- Repeat the task, but dividing by 10, making the number 10 times smaller; for example 30 'bumping' the child holding the 0 away. Ask, *"What happens to the digits when you divide by 10?"* (The digits move one place to the right.) Extend this to decimal numbers.

- Using digit cards ask the children to show you the numbers you call out multiplied by 10. For

example, you call out *"67"* and they show you 670. You could do a similar activity for division – you call out *"450"* and they show you 45.

With the lower-achievers

With adult support

Choose from:

1 Work with the group again on the whole-class starter activity of multiplying by 10. Ask the children to make two- and then three-digit numbers and multiply them by 10. Ask them what their new number is and to explain how it became that, using an abacus.

2 Make some two- and then three-digit multiples of 10. Ask the children to divide their number by 10. What is the new number? How did that happen?

3 Extend all the activities to include decimal numbers.

Teacher-independent activities

Choose from:

1 Give the children copies of Resource sheet 6, 'Multiply by 10'. In the first block, the new number will be 60, so the 6 moves one place to the left.

2 Give the children copies of Resource sheet 7, 'Divide by 10'. Make sure that they appreciate that the digits will now move one place to the right.

Plenary session

- Ask the children what they now know about multiplying and dividing by 10.

- Play 'Swing it'. You need a piece of string about 50cm long and three Unifix or Multilink cubes. Tie the cubes onto one end of the string. Swing the cubes from left to right. When they swing to the right call out a number, for example 3, 67 or 256. The children have to multiply it by 10 mentally and when the cubes swing to the left they call out 30, 670 or 2560. Specific tables or groups can be targeted with certain numbers. If you shorten the string, the swing gets faster and the children need to do some quick thinking!

Ordering

Overall learning objectives

- Use the vocabulary of comparing and ordering numbers, including decimal numbers.

- Give a number lying between two others and order a set of numbers.

- Recognise and extend number sequences formed by counting on and back in steps of any size, including those that go below zero.

- Order a set of negative numbers in context.

- Calculate temperature rise and fall across zero.

Key words

integer	above/below zero
positive	digit
negative	

Ordering

Assessment focus

- Can the children order a set of numbers (including decimals)?

Resources

- digit cards and a number line

- paper-clips

- 12 pieces of A4 paper, each with a three- or four-digit number written on, for example 461, 416, 734, 743, 1479, 1749, 1794, 1497, 1500, 1050, 871 and 817

- Resource sheets 8, 9, 10, 11 and 12

With the whole class

- Tell the children that today they will be learning to order large numbers. Give 12 of them one of the A4-sized numbers each. Ask two of them to jump up and reveal their numbers, for example 461 and 416. The rest of the class should point as quickly as possible to the larger one. Discuss which digits they looked at to help them recognise the larger and why. *"Look at the hundreds first because that is the most significant digit.*

In this case, both are the same so we need to look at the next column, which is the tens column. 60 is bigger than 10 so 461 must be the larger." Repeat this many times, extending to decimal numbers using tenths and hundredths in another lesson. (For more work on decimals, see Chapter 10.)

- Ask five or six of the children to hold up the numbers and order them from smallest to largest. Increase this to ordering up to 10 of the numbers.

- Draw a number line on the board and plot the numbers on it. Ask, *"What number could come between 461 and 416?"*

- Now tell the children they are going to learn how to order decimal numbers. Ask them what a decimal is (part of a whole). Link this to fractions and tenths. Provide copies of the 'Show me' strips from Resource sheet 8 and paper clips. Explain to the children that each line on the strip represents one tenth. Say that one end is 0 and the other is 1. Ask them to position their paper-clips on various decimal places, for example 0.1, 0.7, 0.6 and 0.5 (making links to $\frac{1}{2}$), 0.9 and 0.25.

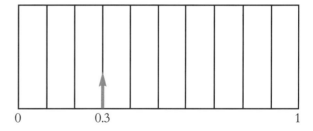

- Now tell them that one end of the strip is 1 and the other is 2. Ask them to put their paper-clips on 1.4, 1.6 and so on. Then invite them to show you the greater number out of two, for example 1.4 and 1.8. Discuss how they know. Ask for a number between 1.4 and 1.8.

- Repeat this activity with hundredths. One end of the strip can be 0.1 and the other end 0.2.

With the lower-achievers

With adult support

Choose from:

1 Using copies of Resource sheets 9 and 10, play the 'Ladders and snakes' game in pairs. Fill in two- and three-digit numbers on Resource sheet 10, such as 75, 91, 700, 912 and 539. Include 1000 as well. Cut out the number cards and mix them up. Tell the children that the bottom of the ladder is 0 and the top is 1000. Explain the rules as follows. Each player takes turns to take one number. They must then try to place their card on the ladder, so that the numbers are ordered from lowest to highest. If the card will not fit, they must put it on the snake and score 1 point against themself. The winner is the player with the fewest cards on the snake. For example:

■ Player 1 picks 399 and places it on the ladder near the bottom.

■ Player 2 picks 901 and places it near the top.

■ Player 1 picks 980 places it at the top.

■ Player 2 picks 967 but there are no spaces on the ladder for it, so it is placed on the snake.

■ Player 1 picks 108 and puts it on the ladder.

■ Player 2 picks 91 and puts it at the bottom.

■ Player 1 picks 75, but it won't fit, so it goes on the snake.

So the game continues. Play several games.

2 Discuss decimal numbers with the group. Ask, *"What are they?"* Use copies of Resource sheet 8 as in the whole-class starter session, asking the children to show you where numbers such as 1.5, 1.7 and 1.8 are, if one end of the strip is 1 and the other is 2. Record this as a group on a large number line.

Teacher-independent activities

Choose from:

1 The 'Ladders and snakes' game can be played if the children know it and can play independently.

2 Again, the 'Ladders and snakes' game can be played if the children know it and can play independently, this time using decimal numbers. In this game, the bottom of the ladder could be 0 and the top 2.

3 Give this group copies of Resource sheet 11. They should write the numbers on the number line in roughly the correct places.

4 Resource sheet 12 is the same activity again but using decimal numbers on a number line.

Plenary session

■ Ask the children to work in pairs and, using their digit cards, make up a three- or four-digit number. Choose some from the pairs to bring their numbers to the front and order them from lowest to highest. Repeat this a few times so that everyone has a go.

■ *"What have you learned today that you didn't know before?"*

■ Play 'Ladders and snakes' again.

Resource sheet 10		
55	75	91
100	108	124
261	399	400
539	589	602
659	700	761
863	865	872
901	912	943
967	980	1000

980
901
399
108
91

Zero and below

Assessment focus

- Can the children recognise and order negative numbers?
- Can the children calculate temperature rise and fall across zero?

Resources

- Resource sheets 13, 14 and 15
- small counters (for example, centicubes), sugar paper ($\frac{1}{4}$ size of full sheet) and pens

With the whole class

- Tell the children that they are going to learn about negative numbers. Begin by finding out what they know about negative numbers. *"Simon, tell me what negative numbers are." "Sarah, when would you see them?"*

- Give out counters and copies of number lines made up from Resource sheet 13 and ask the children to follow your instructions with a small counter. For example, *"Place your counter on 0, move on 5, back 6, on 10, back 12. What number are you on?"* and *"Begin on 7, move back 3, back 8, on 15, on 3, back 16. What number are you on?"*

- Put two rows of six numbers on the board, and ask the children to draw their own number lines and order the numbers from lowest to highest on it. The lower-achievers should order the first six, while the others order all 12. For example:

10	−5	0	1	−6	−15
−12	12	11	−8	−1	−9

  Repeat this a few times.

With the lower-achievers

With adult support

Choose from:

1 Give a copy of Resource sheet 14 to each child. Ask the children to help you to fill in the stars, explaining why they have made their decisions.

Ask them to tell you the differences between various temperatures. Discuss the questions at the bottom of the sheet and answer them together.

2 Using Resource sheet 13, give the children problems to solve about temperature change, similar to those at the bottom of Resource sheet 14, as well as additions and subtractions, for example, *"Start on −5 and go forwards 7."*

Teacher-independent activities

Choose from:

1 Using the number line from Resource sheet 13, invite the children to devise their own problems and answers and write them down. For example, *"If you start on −10, go forward 12, you land on 2."*

2 Give the children copies of Resource sheet 15. The challenge is to draw given positive and negative integers on the number lines.

Plenary session

- Draw a blank number line on the board.

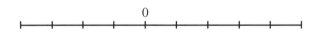

Count on and back in varying steps, such as 2's, 3's, 5's and 10's, going below 0.

- Offer some problems relating to the weather for the children to answer in groups of two, three or four. Give them a time limit of between one and two minutes. Discuss their answers and methods, targeting lower-achievers with the easier questions. Suitable examples could be *"The weather forecaster said that the temperature would drop by 12° overnight. The temperature is now 10°C. What will it drop to?"* or *"Today the temperature hit a high of 12°C. Tomorrow it is expected to rise by another 8°C. What temperature is it expected to be?"* or *"The water in the pan was 15°C. After heating it went up to 46°C. By how much did it increase?"*

Estimating

Overall learning objectives

- Use the vocabulary of estimation and approximation.

- Estimate positions of numbers on a number line.

- Round a two-, three- or four-digit number to the nearest 10, 100 or 1000.

- Estimate answers to calculations.

- Check results of calculations are reasonable.

Key words

almost	approximately equal to
next	estimate
round	guess
nearest	approximate
whole number	calculate
multiple	

Estimation

Assessment focus

- Can the children estimate the position of a number on a number line up to 100/1000?

- Can the children round numbers to the nearest 10/100/1000?

Resources

- Resource sheets 5, 8, 16, 17 and 18

- digit cards, with three extra zero cards for each child

- dice and counters

- paper-clips

With the whole class

- Tell the class that they are going to learn to estimate where numbers go on a number line. Brainstorm what is meant by 'estimation'. Encourage the use of these words – 'almost', 'next', 'round', 'nearest', 'whole number', 'round to the nearest', 'multiple', 'approximately equal to', 'estimate', 'guess' and 'approximate'.

- Draw an unmarked number line on the board. Ask the following types of questions and invite the children to come to the board to help you. *"If one end of the number line is 0 and the other end is 10, put 8 where you think it should go. If one end of the line is 0 and the other 100, put 55 on it."* Ask why rounding numbers to the nearest 10/100/1000 could help this estimation.

- Ask the children to put their paper-clips on various numbers on their 'Show me' strips from Resource sheet 8, and then round to the nearest multiple of 10/100/1000, putting their thumb on the appropriate end. Say, for example, *"If one end of the strip is 30 and the other is 40, put the paper-clip on 37. Now round it to the nearest multiple of 10. If one end of the strip is 200 and the other is 300, put the paper-clip on 230. Now round it to the nearest 100. If one end of the strip is 6000 and the other is 7000, put the paper-clip on 6900. Now round it to the nearest thousand."*

Paper-clip   Thumb

With the lower-achievers

With adult support

Choose from:

1   Ask the children to use the digit cards to round various numbers to the nearest 10, 100 or 1000. For example, for 41 rounded to the nearest 10, the children should show 40 with their digit cards; for 168 rounded to the nearest 100, they should show 200; for 3021 rounded to the nearest 1000, they should show 3000.

2   Refer to the unmarked number line. Say that one end is 0 and the other is 100. Ask them to estimate where various numbers are. Repeat the process, but this time using numbers to 1000.

Teacher-independent activities

Choose from:

1   Use Resource sheet 16 to put numbers on an empty number line. This uses numbers to 100. For higher numbers use Resource sheet 18 and write your own numbers.

2   Use Resource sheet 17 to make a 'Rounding' game for two players, with 15 smiley faces drawn in various places along the track (see the example below). Have available digit cards placed face down on the table, two counters and a dice. Each child takes it in turns to throw the dice and move their counter on the number thrown. If they land on a smiley face, they pick up two digit cards and make a number. The child then rounds their number to the nearest 10 by rounding up or down and then moves on the number of squares indicated by the most significant digit. So, if they pick 34, it is rounded down to 30, and they move on an extra three spaces. Play continues until someone reaches the end of the track. To win, players must have the exact number needed to land on the finishing line.

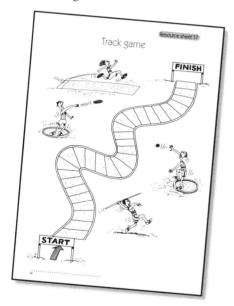

3   Resource sheet 18 is a blank version of Resource sheet 16 which can be used for any numbers you choose for the children to work with.

Plenary session

■   Discuss what has been learned during the lesson and why the children think estimation and approximation might prove to be useful strategies. (This provides a lead-in to the next session.)

■   Play 'Bingo'. Ask the children to fill in 'Bingo' grids from Resource sheet 5 with numbers from 100 to 500. Call out rounded numbers, such as 200, 170 and 350. If a child has a number on

their grid that can be rounded to the one you call out, they cross it out. For example, if you call out 400 and they have, 360, 379 or 401, they can cross it off their grid. The first child to cross all their numbers out (explaining why) is the winner.

A reasonable answer?

Assessment focus

■   Can the children use estimating to aid calculation?

■   Can the children check to see if answers are reasonable?

Resources

■   paper and pens

■   Resource sheets 19, 20 and 21

With the whole class

■   Tell the children that they are going to learn to estimate the answers to calculations. Write a calculation on the board that could be solved by rounding, for example 49 + 101. Ask them to give their methods for solving it. Repeat this a couple of times, emphasising any methods that include rounding.

■   Now write another calculation and ask the children to estimate the answer quickly, using a rounding strategy. For example, for 198 + 71 they could round 198 to 200 and 71 to 70 and then calculate 200 + 70 to give an answer of approximately 270. Ask them to write their estimates on paper. Repeat this exercise, writing some simpler calculations (such as 62 + 29) for the lower-achieving children to do while the others are tackling higher numbers. Remember to include them in the discussion. Work out the correct answers and see how close they were. Repeat this several times. Stress the importance of estimating first, by asking the children why they think this is helpful.

■   Now tell them that they are going to concentrate on checking answers. Write a mixture of correct and incorrect calculations on the board, for example, 19 + 36 = 45, 58 + 69 = 127, 63 – 39 = 36 and 87 – 19 = 72. For each calculation, ask the children to estimate the answer first to see if the one on the board is simila and, then check by their own method to see if they agree with your answer. Ask them to making jottings on scrap paper, to help them remember their thinking. For example, with 19 + 36 = 45, round 19 to 20 and 36 to 40, so the answer should be near 60. The answer on the board isn't, so there is a good chance it is incorrect. Target lower-achievers with appropriate questions. For 87 – 19 = 72, round 87 to 90 and 19 to 20, and the answer should be near 70. The answer on the board is, so it could be correct. This now needs to be checked. They will, of course, discover the answer is wrong. Ask the children to share their methods of solving these calculations.

With the lower-achievers

With adult support

Choose from:

1   Using the skills learned previously, do some solving of word problems with the children. *"Sally had £10. She gave £3.99 to her brother so that he could buy a sticker book. How much did she have left?"* and *"Ben was going shopping for his parents. He had to buy a loaf of bread that cost 78p, 2 litres of milk at 90p and a jar of coffee at £4.99. How much money did he need?"* For each problem, help the children to estimate their answers first and then calculate and check, writing down their estimations and calculations. Finally, note how close the estimate was. In the first problem, Sally gave about £4 to her brother, so she would have around £6 left. (The actual answer is £6.01.) Ask the children to share their methods, for example subtracting £4 and adding on 1p. Check by using another method, such as £10 – £3 = £7, £7 – 99p = £6.01. In the second problem, Ben needed around £1 for the bread, £1 for the milk and £5 for the coffee, so he needed around £7 altogether (the actual answer is £6.67). Ask the children to share their methods, for example 80p + 90p = £1.70, £1.70 + £5 = £6.70. Adjust by taking 3p away (from rounding up) = £6.67. Check by using another method.

2   Use Resource sheet 19, 'Right or wrong?', with the adult giving support by listening to the child and discussing their thinking.

Teacher-independent activities

Choose from:

1   Fill in Resource sheet 20, for estimating answers to calculations. This example is all tens and units but you can use higher numbers.

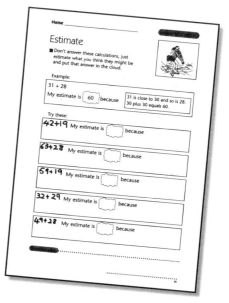

2   Use Resource sheet 21. A key idea behind this activity is to encourage the children to record their thinking using jottings, so there are only three problems. Should you require more, make some up in the same format and invite them to answer them on the other side of the sheet.

Plenary session

■   Play 'True or false?' Verbally give some calculations and their answers, some correct and others incorrect. The children need to put their thumbs up or down, depending on whether they think your statements are correct. Discuss their answers.

■   Ask some quick problems for the children to estimate the answers to, jotting them down. Choose a few children to explain their thinking to the rest of the class.

■   *"Why is it necessary to estimate and check answers? Can you use similar methods in other areas, such as time or measures?"*

Linking addition and subtraction

Overall learning objectives

- Use the relationship between addition and subtraction.
- Check answers by using the inverse operation.
- Partition numbers into H, T and U, adding the most significant digits first.
- Make approximate answers.

Key words

sum of	taking away
total	approximately equal to
reducing	round to the nearest

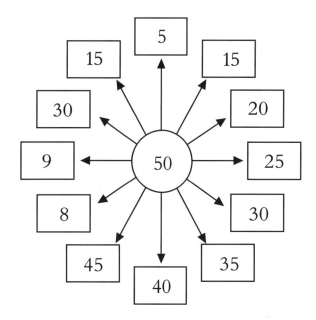

Change it around

Assessment focus

- Do the children understand the relationship between addition and subtraction?
- Can the children check answers by using the inverse operation?

Resources

- digit cards
- Resource sheets 22, 23, 24, 25, 26, 27 and 65
- A3 paper

With the whole class

- Tell the children that they are going to learn about the links between addition and subtraction. Ask, *"What do you know about addition and subtraction?"* Encourage the use of the correct vocabulary ('sum of', 'total', 'reducing' and 'taking away'). Aim towards an understanding of the two rules being opposites and that you can use one to check an answer to a calculation made using the other. Fill in Resource sheets 22 and 23 as shown at the top of the next column. Enlarge them onto A3 paper and display them. These are to be used for work on number bonds to 50 and 100. The idea is for the children to decide what needs to be added to the numbers around the outside to make the number in the middle.

- Point to the numbers around the outsides of the charts, asking the children to call out the other numbers that go with them. For example, if you were pointing to 95, you could express this as *"What do you need to add to 95 to make 100?"* (5) or *"What is the difference between the two numbers?"* (5) Point out that whether you talk about it as addition or subtraction, the answer is the same. In each case, stress the inversion aspect. This very effectively links addition to subtraction.

- Using digit cards, call out other numbers for the children to pair up in a similar way. They need to hold up the correct number using their digit cards. (*"What would you take away from 25 to get 19?"* They hold up 6. *"How did you work out the answer?"*) Target the lower-achievers with specific bonds and keep asking them the same one in order to help them remember that particular fact.

- Say, *"Now you are going to learn how to solve number sentences with missing facts by using your knowledge of the links between addition and subtraction."* Show some half-completed number sentences, for example 54 + ☐ = 70, 89 – ☐ = 67, ☐ – 32 = 43 and ☐ + 27 = 69. Ask the children to work out the missing numbers. Say, *"How did you work it out? Did you have any knowledge that helped you to do this?"* Aim towards the knowledge that addition and subtraction are opposites and that if they know two numbers in a sentence they can use one of these rules to help them. For example, with 54 + ☐ = 70, if 54 plus something is 70, then if you take away the 54 from 70 you can find the missing number. 70 – 54 is 16; therefore 54 + 16 = 70. Ask the children to check. Demonstrate on the board using a blank number line that you fill in.

- Write a range of addition and subtraction sentences on the board, asking the children to work out the missing numbers. Set a time limit. Provide the lower-achievers with tens and units number sentences at this stage. Tell them to draw number lines to help them.

With the lower-achievers

With adult support

Choose from:

1   Using individual copies of Resource sheets 22 and 23, repeat the whole-class activities, making sure the children know by heart all number bonds to 20, 50 and 100.

2   Prepare calculations which make use of inversions for the children to answer and discuss, for example 30 – ☐ = 10, ☐ + 25 = 45 and 32 + ☐ = 60.

3   Give the children copies of Resource sheet 24. Fill it in as shown below and challenge them to to find the missing numbers in the sentences using the number lines to help them.

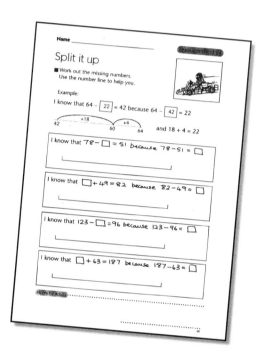

Teacher-independent activities

Choose from:

1   Resource sheet 25 can be used as a 'Dominoes' game with a group or as a link game, either individually or in pairs. The children need to make a circuit of the cards, so that the facts are all arranged correctly, for example:

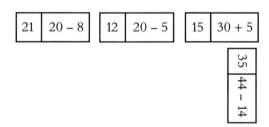

2   Resource sheet 26 contains subtraction calculations. The children must decide which method to use, either counting on (addition) or counting back (subtraction), work out the answers and then check them using the inverse method. Encourage them to use number lines to help. If they have never used number lines they will need support with this activity initially.

3 Fill in Resource sheet 27 with calculations like the example below. The children then fill in the '+' and '–' boxes to make the loop correct. Encourage them to use number lines to help them. Vary the sheet by using another picture from Resource sheet 65 and this time leave different boxes blank.

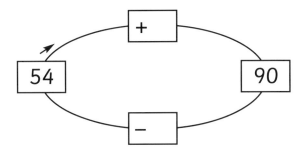

Plenary session

■ *"What are the most useful things that you have learned during today's lesson?"*

■ *"Can you come to the front of the class and demonstrate how we can check answers to addition calculations by subtracting?"*

■ Write some missing-digit calculations on the board and ask the children to work them out. Discuss the methods used. Let them make jottings on paper. Target the lower-achievers with appropriate questions, giving them thinking time and returning to them after asking the other children more difficult calculations.

Estimating and checking

Assessment focus

■ Can the children partition numbers into H, T and U, adding the most significant digits first?

■ Can they make approximate answers?

Resources

■ Resource sheets 3, 28, 29, 30 and 31

■ Resource sheet 31 copied onto acetate

■ OHP and transparent OHP counters

■ place value cards and digit cards

With the whole class

■ Tell the children that they are going to find the answers to addition calculations, approximating first. Ask them what is meant by 'approximate' and how it can be useful in solving calculations (this was covered in the previous chapter). Provide a few examples. Write 57 + 42, then round the numbers to the nearest 10 (60 + 40 = 100) and say, *"So the answer will be about 100. The real answer is 99. 50 + 40 + 7 + 2 = 90 + 9 = 99. How close was the approximation?"*

With the lower-achievers

With adult support

Choose from:

1 Using the place value cards and a large copy of Resource sheet 3, revise the partitioning of numbers, for example 345 = 300 + 40 + 5. Write down some numbers, point to different digits and ask what value they have. Reinforce this by modelling using the place value cards.

2 Encourage the group to add two numbers mentally by partitioning. Concentrate on tens and units numbers initially, for example 26 + 32 = 20 + 30 + 6 + 2 = 50 + 8 = 58.

3 Use Resource sheet 28, which is a problem sheet with mixed addition and subtraction calculations. Ask the children to approximate the answer first, then work it out and finally

find out how close their approximation was. Assistance will be needed as each question has three parts to it.

Teacher-independent activities

Choose from:

1   Give the children copies of Resource sheet 29 which contains two- and three-digit numbers to partition.

2   Let the children complete Resource sheet 30. Give them place value cards to help them.

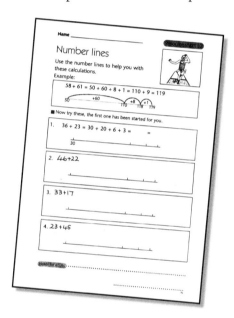

3   Adapt Resource sheet 30 to give slightly harder calculations. Ask *"What is an easy way to add up mentally?"*

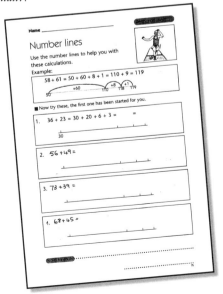

Plenary session

■   *"What is an easy way to add up mentally?"*

■   Put some strings of numbers on the board for the children to calculate mentally and on paper. Provide differentiated questions; for example 34 + 26 + 45, 76 + 46 + 89, and 143 + 234 + 267. Allow extended time for the lower-achievers, returning to them to give their answers after some calculations by the others.

■   Play a 'Stepping stoness' game. Divide the class into teams. Use Resource sheet 31 (as an OHT) filled in with numbers ending in 8 or 9 as shown below. Explain that the aim is for each team to work their way over the stepping stones adding together the numbers they land on. Invite individual children from each team to take turns to come out and, briefed by their team, place a transparent OHP counter on a stepping stone. The children should be encouraged to add by rounding to the nearest 10 and adjusting, which ties in to the work they have been doing on estimating. The winning team is the one to reach the end with the highest score. Only one counter is allowed on a stepping stone at any one time.

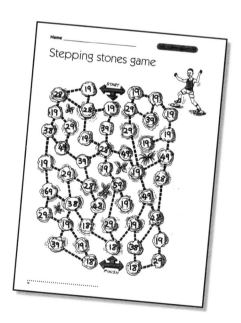

Subtraction

Overall learning objectives

- Use knowledge of number facts and place value to find differences.

- Make approximate answers.

- Extend and refine pencil and paper methods, with approximation.

> ### Key words
>
> subtract   approximate
>
> how did you work   negative
> it out?

Jumping to and fro

Assessment focus

- Can the children subtract 2 two-digit numbers mentally, using a number line for assistance?

- Do the children understand the use of approximation to assist their calculation of difference?

Resources

- blank number lines

- scrap paper and pens for jottings

- Resource sheets 10, 17, 30, 32 and 65

- counters and calculators

- dice

With the whole class

- Write a calculation on the board, for example 136 – 87. Ask the children how they would work out the answer. Several ways are acceptable (if the answer is correct). Say that the method they are going to concentrate on today is the 'counting on' method. Draw the number line below on the board.

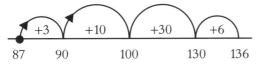

- Demonstrate a few examples, asking the children to copy what you do onto their own number lines. After this, ask them to help you demonstrate solving other calculations on the board or to copy your modelling by themselves.

- As before, ask the children how to find the answer to a subtraction calculation, for example 126 – 75. Ask the lower-achievers first how they would solve it. Again accept all methods that would lead to the correct solution. Explain that this time they will be using a 'counting back' strategy. Draw the number line below on the board to model this method.

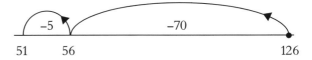

- Demonstrate a few more examples, asking the children to copy what you are doing. Invite some of the class to come to the board either to help you demonstrate (maybe the lower-achievers) or to do the modelling by themselves.

- Write some calculations on the board, for example 95 – 68, 146 – 121 and 325 – 111. The children should approximate the answers and write them on paper to show to the rest of the class. Invite a few of them to explain how they made them. The lower-achievers need to concentrate on the simpler questions. Next ask the children to solve the questions and work out how close they were to their approximations. Ask them why approximating answers could be useful.

With the lower-achievers

With adult support

Choose from:

1 Work with the group on the 'counting on' strategy. (Most children find counting on easier than counting back.) Remind them of what was taught in the first part of the whole-class session. Write some calculations on a piece of paper and then ask them to demonstrate this method using a number line.

2 Repeat the process, but concentrate on the 'counting back' strategy.

3 Play the 'Approximation' game with two to four players, using Resource sheets 10 and 17. Fill in Resource sheet 10 with suitable subtractions such as shown below and cut it into cards. Each child needs some counters. In turn they pick a calculation card and approximate the answer, explaining how they did it. For example, if Player 1 picks 67 – 39, they might decide that the answer is around 30 because 67 can be rounded up to 70, 39 rounded up to 40, and 70 – 40 is 30. The other player should then use a calculator to find the correct answer and work out how close the approximation was. Player 1 then moves their counter on that number of spaces on the board game on Resource sheet 17. (In this case they move on one space as the approximation was only one digit out.) The winner is the last one to reach the end of the track.

Blank cards

98–71	87–61	51–32
79–51	99–48	67–39
83–71	98–79	47–29
97–38	67–18	90–37
47–18	31–12	82–34
87–48	84–38	76–38
107–91	138–109	129–82
117–69	166–119	157–98

Teacher-independent activities

Choose from:

1 Adapt Resource sheet 30 so that it requires children to be able to make two-digit subtraction calculations by counting on using a number line. (Use another picture from the clip art on Resource sheet 65.)

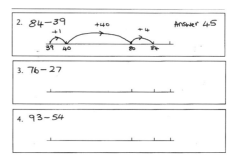

2 Adapt Resource sheet 30 to involve subtracting two-digit numbers from three-digit numbers.

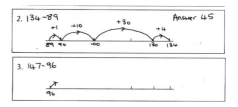

3 Adapt Resource sheet 30 to involve making two-digit subtraction calculations by taking away tens and then units, using a number line.

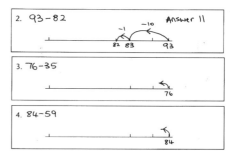

4 Adapt Resource sheet 30 to involve subtracting two-digit numbers from three-digit numbers by taking away tens and then units, using a number line.

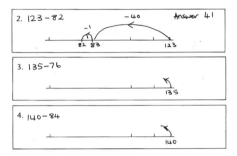

5 Play the 'Back to zero' game, using Resource sheet 32 and two dice. The children take it in turns to throw the dice. One dice represents the tens number and the other the units. Each child makes a two-digit number and writes it in the first box, takes it away from 200 and writes the answer in the second box. This number is then carried to the line below as the starting number. Play continues with the children making numbers using the dice and taking them away from the running total, writing their calculations on the sheet. The winner is the child who gets to, or nearest to, zero by the end of the sheet.

6 After playing the 'Approximation' game (Resource sheets 10 and 17) with an adult, the children could try it on their own.

Plenary session

■ *"Which method of subtraction did you find the easiest to do mentally?"*

■ Ask a few children to describe clearly to everyone else how to do each method of subtraction you have learned this week.

■ *"Why is being able to approximate an answer so important?"*

■ Play the 'Back to zero' game with the whole class, split into teams of three or four. Instead of using the grids, invite some of the children to keep the score for their teams on the board.

From mental to paper

Assessment focus

■ Can the children build on their mental methods to develop their pencil and paper methods?

Resources

■ Resource sheets 3, 33, 34 and 65

■ scrap paper and pens

■ digit cards and place value cards

■ stopwatch/timer

With the whole class

■ Tell the children that they are going to be learning to subtract using a written method, which will help them to answer more difficult calculations. Remind them about partitioning (345 = 300 + 40 + 5) and recombining (300 + 40 + 5 = 345). Write some numbers on the board and ask them to tell you what number each digit actually is, for example *"With the number 3681, what value has the 6?"* (600) Using place value cards and the place value chart from Resource sheet 3, ask the children to put their fingers on certain numbers, such as 4000, 600, 20 and 7, and then tell you what number they can make. Explain that, as with addition, if you partition numbers it can often help you to subtract, for example

358 − 231 =	300	50	8		
	200	30	1		
	100	20	7	=	127

■ Put similar examples on the board and invite some of the children to come and explain how to solve them. At this stage, make sure that your examples don't involve any exchanging or borrowing.

■ The method you will be working on in this part of the lesson will probably make more sense to the lower-achievers, but doesn't naturally lead to the formal algorithm. It is, however, an informal written method that is now approved by the *Numeracy Strategy*. Tell the children that they are going to learn how to subtract using the written method they have just learned but when the numbers don't always seem possible to take away. For example, in the calculation 264 − 128, partitioning into 200 − 100 = 100 and 60 − 20 = 40 works, but what about 4 − 8? Remind them about negative numbers by asking questions such as *"What does 5 − 9 equal?"* (This follows up work completed in Chapter 2.) Demonstrate calculations such as:

$$231 - 114 = \begin{array}{rrr} 200 & 30 & 1 \\ 100 & 10 & 4 \\ \hline 100 & 20 & -3 \end{array}$$

$$= 120 - 3 = 117$$

With the lower-achievers

With adult support

Choose from:

1   Work through some examples of subtraction as done in the first part of the whole-class session. Ask the group to explain to you what they have to do and why.

2   Use calculations that will involve negative numbers in the 'units' column. You could use Resource sheet 33 with the children, making up your own calculations.

3   Ask the children to generate 2 three-digit numbers using their digit cards. They then need to make a subtraction calculation, ensuring the largest number is at the top, and answer it. It is likely that these calculations could be more complex, involving exchanges that you need to supervise. They can record their work on Resource sheet 34.

Teacher-independent activities

Choose from:

1   Fill in Resource sheet 33 with a selection of claculations for the children to do, where they will need to think about negative numbers in the units column. They should work out the answers using the expanded method as shown in the example.

2   Give the children copies of Resource sheet 34 (with another picture from the clip art on Resource sheet 65). This time they have to make up their own calculation using digit cards. This should only be attempted after working with adult support. Sometimes make the negative number in the tens column and sometimes in the units column.

Plenary session

■   Write some calculations on the board and invite a few of the children to come and demonstrate how to use the expanded method to answer them.

■   Did the children think the method of subtraction they have been using makes sense? Why or why not?

■   Play 'Race against the clock'. Write some calculations on the board and give the children a time limit, say two minutes, to answer them. They should use a shorter method (jottings), rather than the expanded method taught, but involving the same principles (for example, 152 − 129 = 100 − 100 = 0, 50 − 20 = 30, 2 − 9 = −7, so the answer is 30 − 7 = 23).

Multiplication

Overall learning objectives

- Recognise multiples of 2, 3, 4, 5, 6, 7, 8, 9, 10, 100 and 1000.

- Develop rapid recall of multiplication facts up to 10 x 10.

- Use known facts to find new ones.

- Use pencil and paper procedures, approximating first, for multiplication of HTU x U and TU x TU.

- Develop a range of vocabulary for multiplication.

Key words

multiple	square number
groups	double
multiply	halve
times	

Different ways to multiply

Assessment focus

- Can the children use a variety of methods to multiply mentally?

- Can the children use a range of vocabulary for multiplication?

- Can the children use facts they already know to make up new ones?

- Can the children recognise multiples of numbers up to 10?

Resources

- large sheet of sugar paper

- counting stick or number line

- multiplication squares with card strips to act as guides

- Resource sheets 5, 22, 23, 35, 36, 37 and 38

- timers/stopwatches

- A3 paper

With the whole class

You might want to teach each different aspect of this lesson separately at first.

- Say, *"Today we will be finding out what you know about multiplication and if you can use facts that you already know to make new facts."* Start by finding out what the children already know about multiplication (including the vocabulary and ways of multiplying) by mind-mapping on a large piece of sugar paper.

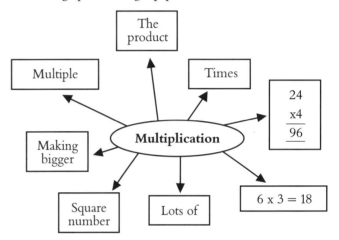

- Count in multiples of 3, 4, 6 and 7, using a counting stick or a number line drawn on the board. Count both up and backwards.

- Call out various multiplication questions (without the answers), directing several to the lower-achievers and giving them extra time to work out the answers. It is worth remembering that some children find it very difficult to remember these facts and can get frustrated by their 'failure' in this. Therefore, let those who are experiencing difficulties use multiplication squares to answer the multiplication questions that you call out. They will probably find it helpful to use card strips as guides.

- Concentrate on one fact, for example 6 x 4 = 24, and ask the children what other facts they know or can find out from this. They should be able to tell you the following: 4 x 6 = 24, 24 ÷ 4 = 6 and 24 ÷ 6 = 4. Ask them what would happen if they doubled the 6 to make 12 x 4. Doubling and halving will increase the number of facts they can work out from the original fact, for example 12 x 4 = 48, 6 x 8 = 48, 12 x 8 = 96, 3 x 4 = 12 and 1.5 x 4 = 6.

■ Explain to the class that they are now going to learn to use facts that they know to calculate more complicated multiplications mentally. Use the clock and flower charts (Resource sheets 22 and 23) to test the children on their ability to call out multiplication and division facts.

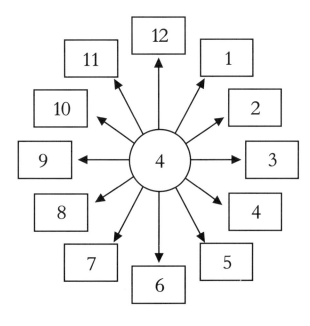

■ On the clock chart, point to the numbers around the clock. Ask the children to multiply them by the number in the middle (in this example 4) and call out the answer. On the flower chart, point to the numbers around the

outside and ask the children to call out the numbers you would divide them by to get the number in the middle (in this example 7), or what you would multiply the number in the middle by to get the number you are pointing at. This helps to reinforce the inversion aspect of multiplication and division.

■ Discuss what the children would do, and why, if the 9 x 4 was 90 x 4 (9 x 4 = 36, so 90 x 4 = 360 because it is 10 times bigger). What about 90 x 40? Repeat this with a few other examples, such as 6 x 4 and 5 x 4.

■ Ask the children how they could now work out what 92 x 4 is. Encourage them to use their knowledge that 90 x 4 = 360 and that 2 x 4 = 8. Therefore 92 x 4 must be (90 x 4) + (2 x 4) which is 368. Repeat this with similar examples, such as 63 x 4 and 52 x 4.

With the lower-achievers

With adult support

Choose from:

1   Use Resource sheet 35. This gives an example of finding more facts from a known one. Go through the example with the children and then fill in three other 'known facts'. Ask them to make as many more facts from these as they can by altering the numbers around and doubling and halving. Lots of discussion is needed with adult support.

2   Resource sheet 36 gives more multiplication facts. The children have to make more by multiplying the digits by 10 and also by partitioning. Again, discussion is needed with adult support.

Teacher-independent activities

Choose from:

1   Copy Resource sheet 37 onto A3 paper and write in some multiplications as a 'Facts challenge', as in the example shown at the top of the first column on the next page. This is a timed game for two players. Player 1 works on the two stars on the left and Player 2 the two stars on the right. They look at one of the facts on the sheet and are given one minute to write down within the star shapes as many others as

they can make from them. They then compare facts and agree on whether or not they are correct. They score one point for each fact. The winner is the player with the most points.

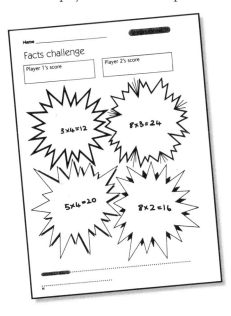

2   Ask the children to make up their own clock charts using Resource sheet 22 for the 3, 4 and 5 times tables on large sheets of coloured paper to show the rest of the class during the plenary session.

3   Use Resource sheet 38 in groups of two to four to form a multiplication loop with the 'Dominoes' cards. The children can be encouraged to use their multiplication square to find the facts that they don't know.

Plenary session

■   Write a calculation on the board (such as 7 x 6 = 42) and ask the children to think of as many facts related to it as possible. Invite them to write them on the board in a brainstorming fashion.

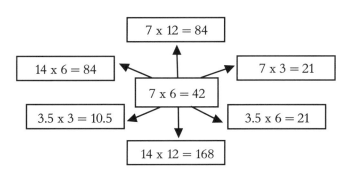

■   Play a game of 'Bingo' using Resource sheet 5. Ask the children to fill it in with multiples of 3, 4, 7 and 8 (the lower-achievers can use tables squares for support). Call out multiplication questions (without answers). If the children have the answers on their grids they can cross them out. The first child to cross out all their numbers is the winner.

■   Return to the mind map made at the beginning of the session and ask the children what can now be added to it.

Pencil and paper multiplication

Assessment focus

■   Can the children use pencil and paper methods to solve multiplication calculations?

Resources

■   Resource sheets 39, 40 and 41

■   paper and pens

■   multiplication squares

With the whole class

■   Tell the children that they are going to learn how to multiply large numbers using the grid multiplication method. Remind them of the previous lesson when they partitioned numbers to multiply them, for example 43 x 6 = 240 + 18 = 258 (40 x 6 + 3 x 6). Write some similar calculations on the board and invite some of them, including the lower-achievers, to come to the board and answer them. You might have to act as scribe for the latter group.

■   Explain that with larger numbers, grid multiplication might be more efficient. Demonstrate this on the board using a simple calculation first, such as 27 x 3.

	20	7
3	60	21

Answer = 81

Move on to slightly more complicated calculations where the grid method would obviously be clearer and more efficient, for example 43 x 24. Explain the partitioning and demonstrate on the board.

	40	3	
20	800	60	860
4	160	12	172

Answer = 860 + 172 = 1032

Repeat this with a variety of simple and then more complicated examples.

With the lower-achievers

With adult support

Choose from:

1   Work with the children on grid multiplications as in the whole-class session. Use large paper and thick pens, and ask them to help you write out and answer the calculations, discussing what is happening at each stage.

2   Give them copies of Resource sheet 39, which offers problem-solving exercises using grid multiplication.

Teacher-independent activities

Choose from:

1   Use Resource sheet 40 to make some two-digit by single-digit multiplications. The children can use their multiplication squares if they wish.

37 x 3

	30	7
3		

45 x 7

	40	5
7		

32 x 4

	30	2
4		

2   Give the children copies of Resource sheet 41 which requires them to make up suitable multiplication problems using given numbers.

Plenary session

■   Choose a variety of calculations and ask the children to come out to the front to demonstrate how they calculated their answers using the grid multiplication method.

■   Ask individuals what they found easy about the work they have been doing and what they found difficult.

■   Make up some problems for the children to answer, for example *"When class 6 went to the zoo, the 32 children bought ice creams which cost 74p each. How much did they spend altogether?"* Let them work them out on paper if they wish. Invite a few children to come to the board to demonstrate what they did.

Multiplication and division

Overall learning objectives

- Consolidate an understanding of multiplication and division and their effects on and relationship to each other.
- Begin to use brackets and use related vocabulary.

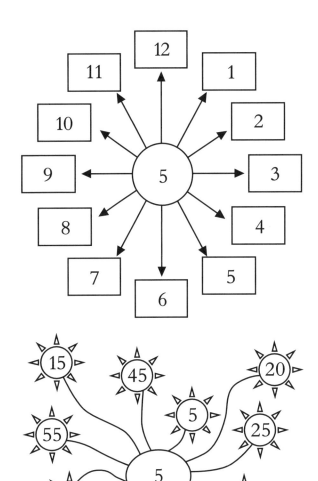

> **Key words**
>
> | | |
> |---|---|
> | product | factor |
> | multiply | quotient |
> | inverse | prime number |
> | divide | square number |
> | divisible by | square root number |

Making links

Assessment focus

- Do the children understand that division is the inverse of multiplication?
- Can the children understand and use the vocabulary related to multiplication and division?

Resources

- Blu-tack and card
- Resource sheets 5, 10, 17, 22, 23, 42 and 43
- sets of digit cards
- multiplication squares
- counters

With the whole class

- Begin by telling the class that they are going to investigate the links between multiplication and division. Use Resource sheets 22 and 23 as shown at the top of the next column to practise multiplication and division facts (see Chapter 6). Begin with the 5 times table as the children should know this well and the inversion emphasis of the lesson can be taught very simply using a table that they are familiar with.

- Write a times table fact on the board and invite three children to come to the front and write the other three facts that go with it. So, for 6 x 5 = 30, they would need to write 5 x 6 = 30, 30 ÷ 5 = 6 and 30 ÷ 6 = 5. Repeat this activity. Discuss how they can use this knowledge to calculate such questions as ☐ x 5 = 45 and ☐ ÷ 5 = 12.

- Extend this to larger multiples of 5, for example ☐ x 5 = 85, 5 x ☐ = 125, 75 ÷ 5 = ☐ and ☐ ÷ 5 = 16.

- Now tell the children that they are going to look at the links between multiplication and division through the 7 times table and find out what else this knowledge can help with. Use Resource sheets 22 and 23 again. Repeat the previous exercise, asking *"If we know 6 x 7 = 42, what else do we know?"* The children should be able to respond with 7 x 6 = 42, 42 ÷ 6 = 7 and 42 ÷ 7 = 6. Write some calculations on the board for them to answer and explain, for example ☐ ÷ 7 = 8, 7 x ☐ = 84, ☐ x 7 = 70 and ☐ ÷ 7 = 15. Extend their thinking by asking what facts from other times tables this knowledge can help us with, for example 9 times tables because if we know that 9 x 7 = 63, we know that 7 x 9 = 63 and 63 ÷ 9 = 7. These links are important to make.

■ Explain that they are going to learn about the special vocabulary relating to multiplication and

division. First rehearse the multiplication and division facts from the 7 times table. Introduce these terms: 'factor', 'product', 'quotient', 'prime', 'square' and 'square root' in relation (where possible) to the 7 times table. This open-ended activity could take place over two lessons and every child can contribute. Write the terms on pieces of card and Blu-tack them to the board. Invite the children to the front to brainstorm or mind-map around the words, explaining what they are doing. Encourage them to think of as many examples as possible.

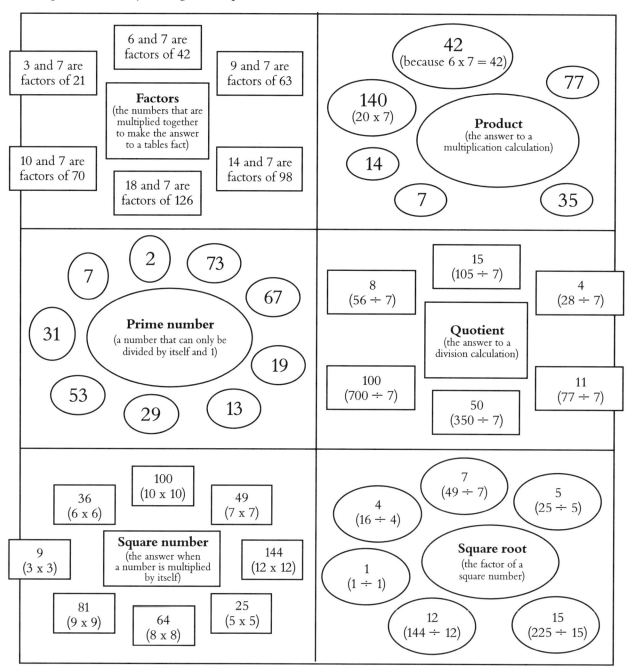

With the lower-achievers

With adult support

Choose from:

1   Use the clock chart for the 5 times table to revise inversions. Ask questions such as *"What do we multiply 5 by to get 45?"* and *"What do we divide 30 by to get 6?"*

2   Work with the group, revising the vocabulary introduced during the whole-class session by reviewing each word and giving an example. Ask the children to write down or tell you as many more examples as they can think of in a given time, maybe two minutes. For example, 2 and 4 are factors of 8. 1, 2, 3, 4, 6 and 12 are all factors of 12.

Teacher-independent activities

Choose from:

1   Use Resource sheet 42, which offers the children division challenges using halving.

2   Photocopy Resource sheet 10 onto card. Write on a number of multiplications and their division inversions, as shown below. Cut it up into individual playing cards. Use them for a 'Snap' game, where the first player lays down a card and the next player lays one on top. When one player lays down a card with the inverse calculation (x or ÷) the first player to shout *"Snap!"* wins the pile. Play continues until one player has won all the cards or, if it is a timed activity, the time runs out.

Blank cards		Resource sheet 10
2 × 6	6 × 2	12 ÷ 2
12 ÷ 6	5 × 6	6 × 5
30 ÷ 5	30 ÷ 6	6 × 4
4 × 6	24 ÷ 6	24 ÷ 4

3   Fill in Resource sheet 43 with a number in the centre of each diagram. Ask the children to find as many factors of the numbers as they can. Give them between five to ten minutes to play. The winner is the child to find the most factors in the given time.

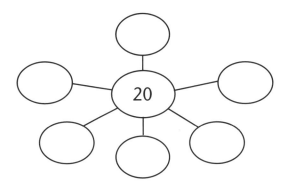

4   Use Resource sheet 17 to play the 'Product' game. Give each player a multiplication square. Place two sets of digit cards face down. The first player picks two digit cards and calculates their product. Then the other players use their multiplication squares to check the answer. If the first player is correct they move their counter two places along the game board. The winner is the player to reach the finish first, or the player ahead when the time runs out.

Plenary session

■   Hold up the vocabulary words that you have been focusing on during the lesson and ask the children to explain their meaning and give examples.

■   Write some multiplication and division facts on the board and invite the children to come and write some other related facts.

■   Play 'Bingo'. Have prepared copies of Resource sheet 5 with a selection of answers to the 5 and 7 times tables. Give each child a copy. As you call out two factors the children check their sheets and if the product is there they can cross it out. The first player to cross out all their numbers is the winner.

■   Discuss the successes of the lesson. Invite some of the children to tell the others what they have learned. Make sure you include the lower-achievers. Display their successes on a poster as shown overleaf and add to it during the series of lessons. Ensure that everyone gets their name on for any success, however small – to the child it is still very valuable.

This week we are learning about the links between multiplication and division

Peter and Jenny now know what a square root is and can explain it to the class.

Katie now knows that if she knows 5 x 7 = 35, she also knows what you get if you divide 35 by 7.

Sam, Sarah, Tracey and Ben know what the products of different numbers are. They played the 'Product' game.

We have succeeded!

Ben   Adam   Maggie

■ Adapt the 'Bingo' game to focus on factors. Let the children fill in the grids from Resource sheet 5 with a selection of numbers from 1 to 20. Call out some products from various multiplication tables, maybe the 2, 3, 4, 5, 7 and 10 times tables, and ask them to cross out any factors they have on their grids. So, if you call out 36, they can cross out 1, 2, 3, 4, 6, 9, 12 and 18 if they have them on their grid. When there is a winner, go through their numbers, asking them to explain why they crossed each one out.

Brackets

Assessment focus

■ Can the children understand why brackets are needed?

Resources

■ Resource sheets 44 and 45

■ a selection of calculators

With the whole class

■ Begin by saying, *"Today you are going to learn why brackets are important for working out calculations."* Write some calculations, such as 5 x 6 + 4, 9 + 21 ÷ 3 and 10 – 8 x 2, on the board. Ask the children to tell you the possible answers. They are most likely to give one easily and need prompting for the second. For example, for 5 x 6 + 4, they are most likely to say *"5 x 6 = 30, then add on 4, which equals 34."* Explain that it could also be 5 x the sum of 6 + 4, which equals 50. Ask, *"How do we know which it is?"* The answer is that we don't, so to make it clear we need to use brackets. Brackets show us what part of the calculation to do first. Explain the calculation using brackets.

(5 x 6) + 4 = 34

5 x (6 + 4) = 50

Do the same with the other calculations.

(9 + 21) ÷ 3 = 10

9 + (21 ÷ 3) = 16

and

(10 – 8) x 2 = 4

10 – (8 x 2) = –6

■ Put this idea into a problem format by saying, *"At Scout camp there were 6 tents. Each had 5 Scouts sleeping in them. During the camp, 10 more Scouts joined the group. How many Scouts were there altogether?"* Ask the children how they would work this calculation out. Note what they say on the board in numbers and symbols. They might say something like this: *"Well, if there are 6 tents and each had 5 Scouts, that would be 6 x 5, which is 30. Then another 10 came, so you would add* that on, which would make 40 altogether." Write up 6 x 5 + 10. Ask the children what two answers this number sentence could have. They are 6 x 5 and then add 10 = 40, or 6 x the sum of 5 + 10 = 90. Discuss what should be done to avoid confusion. (Use brackets.) Invite a child to the board to put the brackets in the correct place; (6 x 5) + 10.

With the lower-achievers

With adult support

Choose from:

1   Write some calculations on a piece of paper, for example 3 x 2 + 6. Discuss the two possible answers. Ask one of the children to write the calculation again, putting brackets around the 3 x 2. Ask a question that would fit the equation, such as *"There were 3 girls who each had 2 books. They borrowed 6 more from the library, so how many did they have then?"* Repeat the process with brackets around the 2 + 6.

2   Using lots of different calculators, let the children find out which ones automatically put brackets around multiplications. For example some calculators will do 2 + 6 x 3 as 2 + (6 x 3) = 20, but very simple calculators will do the calculation in order, 2 + 6 = 8 x 3 = 24.

Teacher-independent activities

Choose from:

1   Give the children copies of Resource sheet 44. They have to work out the two possible answers for each question.

2   Give the children copies of Resource sheet 45. This time they have to put in the brackets to make the calculations correct.

Plenary session

■   Write some calculations on the board and invite several children to come to the front and put in the brackets to make the calculations correct, for example 5 x 7 – 3 = 20, 10 + 15 ÷ 5 = 5 and 20 – 8 x 2 = 4.

■   Make up some problems for the children to solve and invite them to come to the front to write the calculation on the board and explain their thinking. Say, for example, *"The 2 minibuses*

each carried 14 people. They were nearly full, with just 2 spare seats. How many people were travelling on the buses altogether?"* They need to decide what is intended by the question. It could either be that there are 2 spare seats in each minibus, (14 – 2) x 2, or that there are just 2 spare seats altogether, (2 x 14) – 2.

Division

Overall learning objectives

- Use a variety of methods for division.

- Use approximation when calculating divisions.

- Investigate a mathematical statement and find examples that satisfy it.

- Begin to give a quotient as a fraction.

Key words

approximate	remainder
divide	quotient
halve	divisor

Division

Assessment focus

- Can the children use a variety of methods for division?

Resources

- scrap paper and pens

- Resource sheets 5, 46, 47 and 48

- digit cards

- counters

- Resource sheet 47 copied onto acetate

- OHP

With the whole class

- Tell the children that they are going to learn to divide using quick methods, mentally or with jottings. Write a calculation on the board, for example 48 ÷ 4. Ask them to answer this and explain how they did it. Write their answers on the board as shown at the top of the next column.

> I knew 4 x 12 is 48, so 48 ÷ 12 must be 4. We did this last time!!

> I knew 40 ÷ 4 is 10 and 8 ÷ 4 is 2. 10 and 2 is 12, so that's the answer.

> I halved 48 and halved it again.

> 48 ÷ 4

> I took away groups of 4. I knew that if I took away 10 groups of 4 I would be left with 8, which is 2 groups. Altogether that makes 12 groups.

For this session, focus on easy division methods, such as halving and halving again, simple partitioning and using multiplication facts.

- Tell the children that they will now be focusing on division by 2, 4 and 8. Ask them if they can think of a quick way of doing this. They should be able to tell you to halve in order to divide by 2. They may, with some prompting, tell you to halve and halve again to divide by 4 and halve and halve and halve again for 8. Put some appropriate numbers on the board that can be halved, and ask them to divide the numbers by 2, 4 and 8.

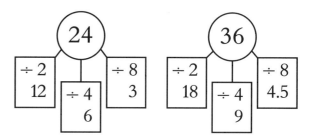

- Ask the children how they can solve calculations that aren't divided by 2, 4, or 8, such as 36 ÷ 9. The answer you are aiming for is the fact that they know that 9 x 4 = 36, so 36 ÷ 9 must be 4. This is a reminder of previous work. Use a partitioning approach when it is possible, for example for 69 ÷ 3, 60 ÷ 3 = 20 and 9 ÷ 3 = 3, so 69 ÷ 3 must be 23. Stress that this isn't always possible, but could be considered when it is.

- Now write a selection of calculations on the board, such as 48 ÷ 2, 60 ÷ 4, 93 ÷ 3 and 27 ÷ 3. Target specific ones for the lower-achievers (maybe concentrate on dividing by 2 and 4 as this is the focus of the lesson) and ask the children to think about the best way to solve them. They might find it easier to jot down their ideas in order to remember them.

■ Say, *"Now we are going to learn how to divide mentally by grouping."* Write a simple calculation on the board, for example 39 ÷ 3. Discuss groups of 3 and how many there are in 39. Say, *"10 groups of 3 are 30 and 3 groups of 3 are 9, so 13 groups of 3 are 39."* Use several examples like this and then extend the activity to using more complicated numbers, such as 327, where you could say *"There are 100 groups of 3 in 300 and 9 in 27; therefore there are 109 in 327, so 327 ÷ 3 = 109."* Remember that while you are modelling it is important to involve the children in helping you.

With the lower-achievers

With adult support

Choose from:

1   Use Resource sheet 46 and play a halving game. This involves using digit cards to make up numbers. (You could use just even numbers to make the game easier.) Let each child choose two cards and make a number. The idea of the game is to attempt to divide their number by up to 8 by halving but keeping to whole numbers. If they can only divide by 2, they move their counter along the game board one flag. If they can divide by 4, they move along two flags. If they can divide by 8, they move three flags along the board. If they can't go, however, the next player has a turn. For example, with 40 they could halve this to 20 and halve again to get 10 and again to get 5. This will be dividing by 8 and gives the child three moves. The winner is the player who helps Martin down the ski slope!

2   Work with the children on the strategy of grouping. Write a calculation on a large sheet of paper, for example 68 ÷ 6. Encourage them to group the 10's first. 10 groups of 6 are 60 leaving 8, which gives one group of 6 and 2 left over. The answer will be 11 with 2 left over. Repeat this several times with different calculations.

Teacher-independent activities

Choose from:

1   Use Resource sheet 47. Choose a particular divisor for the children to use – this should be simple, such as 5, then they can play this independently. They need to take turns to make up two-digit numbers using digit cards and work out the number of whole groups of 5 that they can make out of each number. So if the digits 2 and 7 were picked, and the number chosen 27, this would have 5 whole groups of 5 in it. If the child is correct and the other players agree, the child puts a counter on the corresponding number on the game board, in this case 5. The aim of the game is to cover as many squares as possible. There will be occasions when there are no appropriate numbers available on the board, in which case the child will have to wait until their next turn.

2   Use Resource sheet 48 to suit your children. Write some calculations in the boxes for them to work with, as shown below.

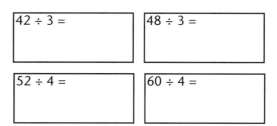

| 42 ÷ 3 = | 48 ÷ 3 = |
| 52 ÷ 4 = | 60 ÷ 4 = |

They need to work out how many groups of the divisor there are in the given numbers. Remind them that 'groups of 10' is the best starting point to work from.

Plenary session

■ Play the 'Grouping' game with the class, using a transparency of Resource sheet 47. Divide the class into four groups to play. Having agreed the divisor, you call out a two-digit number, the groups discuss and agree how many of the divisor are in that number and the appointed speakers for the groups put up their hands to answer. Colour in the numbers according to the group that answered correctly. Which group's colour appears most at the end?

- Write a variety of calculations on the board. Ask the children to solve them and explain their methods while you scribe their answers.

> I know that
> 8 x 8 is 64.

> I knew that 5 groups of 8 gets rid of 40, leaving 24 and 3 groups of 8 is 24, so 8 groups of 8 are 64.

> I halved it, halved it a second time and halved it again and got 8.

> $64 \div 8$

> I took 60 and divided it by 8 by halving 3 times. This gave me $7\frac{1}{2}$. So, there are $7\frac{1}{2}$ 4's in 60. I took the $\frac{1}{2}$ (which is 4) and added it to the other 4 to give me 8. I divided that by 8 and got 1. So 7 add 1 is 8 and $64 \div 8 = 8$.

Aim to get them to give several of the methods taught and discuss which is the most efficient for the numbers given.

- Ask the children to double and halve numbers that you call out using digit cards to show their answers. Differentiate your questioning by asking the lower-achievers to double and halve, while the others double and halve twice or three times, depending on their ability.

- Play 'Bingo'. Ask the children to fill in the grids from Resource sheet 5 with quotients (answers) from the 2, 4 and 8 times table. Call out calculations such as $24 \div 4$; if they have the answer they cross it out. The first one to cross out all their numbers wins.

Remainders

Assessment focus

- Can the children give the remainder in a quotient as a fraction?

Resources

- paper and pencils/pens
- Resource sheets 49 and 50
- digit cards
- 40 counters per pair
- tables square

With the whole class

- Begin by telling the children that they are going to learn about remainders and how to make them into fractions. Write a calculation on the board, for example $89 \div 8$. Ask them to solve this using the grouping method. Talk it through with them. *"10 groups of 8 make 80. There are 9 left, and 1 group of 8 makes 8, leaving 1. So there are 11 groups of 8 and 1 left."* Discuss what the one left is. Aim towards the understanding that one out of a group of 8 can be written as $\frac{1}{8}$. Do several examples like this, including a few more complicated ones for the higher-achieving children. Each time ask them specific questions in order to encourage their thinking along the right lines. Invite some of them to explain a complete calculation to everyone else. Include in this some targeted examples that they work out by themselves with paper and pencil and explain after a time limit.

- Say, *"Now we are going to solve division problems that involve remainders."* Ask the children a problem. For example, *"I had 50 sweets. I wanted to share them equally between my 3 friends and myself. How many did I have left?"* Again, use the grouping method for the division, encouraging them to think of the largest group that they can to take away. *"I know 12 groups of 4 are 48, so each child will have 12 and there will be 2 sweets left over."* Several targeted examples need to be worked through.

With the lower-achievers

With adult support

Choose from:

1   Prepare Resource sheet 49, 'What's left over?'
    The children need to solve division calculations
    and give the remainders as fractions. Use
    examples such as shown below.

31 ÷ 3 =	38 ÷ 3 =
49 ÷ 4 =	43 ÷ 4 =

2   Set up some word problems for the group to do
    with adult help. For example, 103 biscuits to
    share between 50 children and 52 pence to
    share between 2 children. Focus on the
    remainder as a fraction.

Teacher-independent activities

Choose from:

1   In pairs, let the children play a game using
    Resource sheet 50. Choose a divisor for them
    to use, such as 3. Give them digit cards to
    generate two-digit numbers. Then ask them to
    divide them by 3 and work out what the
    remainder is. They then collect however many
    counters correspond with their remainder and
    place them in their 'running shoe' on the sheet.
    Keep the game going until the 'collectable'
    counters (about 40) have all been used. The
    winner is the child with the most counters on
    their shoe. Encourage the children to check
    each other's answers.

2   Play the game as described above but with a
    different divisor.

Plenary session

■   Ask various children who have been warned to
    explain the work that they have been doing.

■   Ask the children to show the remainders of
    division calculations as quickly as they can using
    digit cards. Pace the activity so that the lower-
    achievers work on one question while the
    others are answering up to three.

■   Discuss remainders with the children. Ask
    questions such as *"What does a remainder show us?"*
    and *"Why do we put remainders into fractions?"* (To
    show that the remainder is 1, 2, and so on out
    of a group of another number.) Then go on to
    tell them what they will be doing in the next
    session. (The progression in Chapter 9 is to
    write remainders as decimal fractions.)

■   Play the game on Resource sheet 50 with the
    whole class divided into teams. The lower-
    achievers will have played this and can explain
    the rules to the others.

Chapter 9

Fractions and percentages

Overall learning objectives

■ Recognise from practical experience when two simple fractions are equivalent.

■ Change an improper fraction to a mixed number.

■ Begin to understand % sas a fraction of 100.

■ Use fraction notation and relate this to decimals.

> ### Key words
>
> proper/improper fraction   equivalent
>
> mixed number   percentage
>
> numerator   per cent
>
> denominator

Fractions

Assessment focus

■ Can the children recognise equivalent fractions?

■ Can the children compare and order fractions?

■ Can the children begin to change improper fractions to mixed numbers?

Resources

■ clocks

■ clock stamp copied onto paper and OHT

■ card circles cut into the following fractions of the OHT clock: halves, quarters, thirds, sixths, ninths and twelfths

■ fraction strips and fraction cards

■ OHP

■ large pieces of coloured paper and A3 paper, scissors and glue

■ counters and dice

■ Resource sheets 51, 52, 53, 54, 55 and 56

With the whole class

■ Begin by saying *"Today we are going to learn about equivalent fractions."* Ask the children what is meant by the word 'equivalent'. Lead them to understand that it means things that are 'the same'.

■ Tell the children to move the hands on their clocks to divide them in half. Demonstrate this by displaying a clock face and covering half of it with card. Explain that you have split the clock into two parts and covered one of those two parts. This can be shown with the hands on 12 and 6.

■ Encourage them to show a quarter on their clocks by putting the hands on the 12 and 3 or, for the more able, other numbers. Demonstrate this using a quarter circle, again explaining that the clock has now been split into four equal parts and that one of them has been covered.

■ Challenge the children to demonstrate some other points on the clock face where they can make a quarter, for example 1 and 4, 6 and 9 and 11 and 2.

■ Demonstrate how two quarters make a half, four quarters make a whole, and two halves make a whole. Stress the word 'equivalent' each time and say that you have split or divided the clock into so many equal parts and covered one or more of them.

■ Repeat this with thirds, sixths and twelfths, each time using the clock face and covering it with the card pieces you have prepared. Each time look at the equivalences between them – sixths and twelfths; thirds, sixths and twelfths. With each one, stress how many are needed to cover the whole clock, for example 12 twelfths.

■ Say, *"Now we are going to compare and order fractions."* Use the clock and card pieces to remind the children what fractions the pieces are. Order them from smallest to largest; $\frac{1}{12}$, $\frac{1}{6}$, $\frac{1}{4}$, $\frac{1}{3}$, $\frac{1}{2}$, 1 whole. Draw a number line on the board and plot them on it.

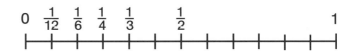

■ Use a selection of fraction pieces, for example $\frac{2}{3}$, $\frac{1}{2}$, $\frac{3}{4}$ and $\frac{5}{6}$, and ask the children to guess their correct order and write them down in order from smallest to largest. Increase the number of fractions for the more able children. Draw a line on the board and invite a few of them to put their guesses on it. Discuss their results. Demonstrate and compare the sizes using the card pieces. Repeat this using other combinations of the fractions.

■ Repeat the process using fraction strips for halves, quarters, eighths, fifths and tenths. Compare and order a selection of these fractions, and write them on a number line.

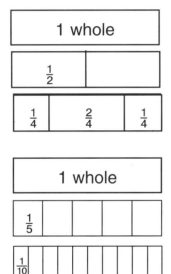

■ Now tell the children that they are going to learn how to change improper fractions into mixed numbers. Write the improper fraction $\frac{3}{2}$ on the board. Ask the children what it means. Aim towards the answer that some things have been split into two equal parts and that three of those halves have been covered/taken/used. Ask *"Is this possible? Can you draw this on the board? How can you solve the problem?"* Discuss the possibility of needing at least two whole things in order to take three halves. Draw a diagram of this on the board. Explain that this is called an improper fraction because it involves whole things plus parts of a whole. Repeat the process with $\frac{4}{2}$, $\frac{5}{4}$, $\frac{6}{4}$ and so on.

With the lower-achievers

With adult support

Choose from:

1   Give each child six copies of a clock outline. Ask them to cut one into half from the numbers 12 to 6 and stick it onto one side of a large piece of paper. Ask them to do the same thing to another for a quarter, another for a third, a sixth, a ninth and a twelfth, labelling each one. Ask them to look carefully at them and decide which is the smallest, the next smallest and so on to the largest. Once they have decided, ask them to plot them on a number line on A3 paper.

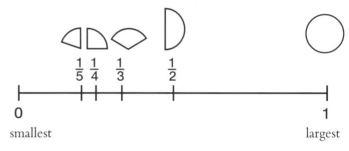

With their spare pieces, they should cut out and stick onto paper all the equivalences to $\frac{1}{2}$; $\frac{2}{4}$, $\frac{3}{6}$, $\frac{6}{12}$ and plot these onto a second number line.

2   Using the clock outlines, ask the children to cut out and glue onto large sheets of coloured paper the following fraction equivalences: $\frac{1}{3}$ and $\frac{2}{6}$, $\frac{6}{12}$ and $\frac{1}{2}$, $\frac{3}{4}$ and $\frac{9}{12}$. Ask them to make up some more.

3   Give the children fraction strips and ask them to label the parts with the appropriate fraction. Give them a selection of about five fraction cards and tell them to order them using the strips to help, as demonstrated in the whole-class session. Finally, they should write the fractions in the correct order on a number line.

Teacher-independent activities

Choose from:

1   Repeat the above exercise a few times, encouraging the children to work independently.

2   Use Resource sheets 51 and 52 for pairs to play a game. Each player has a strip divided into eighths. They take turns to turn over fraction

cards and place the appropriate number of counters on their strips; so $\frac{1}{8}$ would be 1 counter, $\frac{1}{4}$ would be 2 counters, and so on. The winner is the player who fills their strip first.

3 Resource sheets 53 and 54 offer another version of the game described above, this time focusing on twelfths.

4 Use Resource sheet 55 to focus on proper fractions. The children have to write in the empty box the fraction that is shaded.

5 Resource sheet 56 requires them to shade in the given improper fraction.

Plenary session

■ Ask the children to use dice to generate numbers to make fractions. Write on the board the fractions they have made. For example, one child might throw a 4, and another a 5, which when put together as a fraction make $\frac{4}{5}$. A second pair might throw a 3 and a 2 which make $\frac{2}{3}$. Use the smaller number thrown as the numerator and the higher as the denominator. Once five or six fractions have been made, discuss their order and write them on a number line on the board. Involve lower-achievers by asking them to help you generate the numbers and write the fractions on the board. This can be used as a consolidation/assessment activity.

■ Repeat the process, but this time making improper fractions by using the higher number thrown as the numerator. With the class, change the improper fractions into mixed numbers and plot them on a number line.

■ Repeat the activity again, this time making the numerator the first number thrown, so that a mixture of vulgar and improper fractions are made. Discuss the fractions and plot them on a number line.

■ Ask the lower-achievers to present their work for the session, particularly if they have played the game using Resource sheet 53. Invite them to play the game with the rest of the class (split into four). Draw the grids on the board and let them shade them in appropriately.

■ Summarise what has been learned during the session, using lots of discussion, questioning and listening.

Percentages

Assessment focus

■ Can the children understand the relationship between fractions and percentages?

■ Do the children understand that a % is a fraction of 100?

Resources

■ Resource sheet 57 copied onto acetate and three copies on card (one left as a whole, and the others cut into smaller percentages, such as 50%, 25%, 20% and 10%)

■ OHP

■ small cubes

■ Resource sheets 5, 10, 17, 57, 58 and 59

■ card and scissors

■ counters

■ materials for making a poster

With the whole class

■ Tell the children that they are going to learn about the relationship between fractions and percentages. Use Resource sheet 57, copied onto acetate to use on an OHP, and the card copies (see Resources above) to demonstrate the fact that a % is a fraction of 100. Cover up the % grid with the 'whole' card. Explain that the whole card is equal to 100% and that each % is of equal size. Make a link with fractions by putting a small cube on one of the % squares, and asking the children to tell you what fraction it would be. Lead them to say that it is 1 out of 100 or $\frac{1}{100}$. Now cover up two squares. What is the fraction? Repeat this several times with different percentages. Make a list on the board to show these equivalences.

Percentage	Fraction
1%	$\frac{1}{100}$
2%	$\frac{2}{100}$
5%	$\frac{5}{100}$
10%	$\frac{10}{100}$
15%	$\frac{15}{100}$

- Use the card parts of Resource sheet 57 to cover up 50% of the grid. Ask what fraction has been covered. Encourage the answers $\frac{50}{100}$ and $\frac{1}{2}$. Repeat the process with the quarter piece, fifth piece and tenth piece in the same way. Fill in a table on the board.

Percentage	Fraction	Fraction
50%	$\frac{50}{100}$	$\frac{1}{2}$
25%	$\frac{25}{100}$	$\frac{1}{4}$
20%	$\frac{20}{100}$	$\frac{1}{5}$
10%	$\frac{10}{100}$	$\frac{1}{10}$

- Using the % square acetate on the OHP and some cubes, cover up different numbers of squares. Ask the children to tell you what percentage of the square is covered. Then ask them to tell you what fraction is covered in as many ways as they can. For example, 20 squares covered up $= 20\% = \frac{20}{100} = \frac{10}{50} = \frac{2}{10} = \frac{1}{5}$. Ask the lower-achievers for their contributions first, expecting them to be able to tell you at least 20% and $\frac{20}{100}$.

With the lower-achievers

With adult support

Choose from:

1   Give pairs of children three copies of Resource sheet 57. Ask them to cut out fraction shapes from two of them as you did for the whole-class session, and place each of them in turn over the % square to see what fractions and percentages match (such as $\frac{1}{2} = 50\%$). Help them to label the pieces, perhaps with different-coloured crayons. They can then complete the table on Resource sheet 58.

2   Order the percentage pieces from a whole, a half, a quarter and so on. Demonstrate how easy percentages can be, for example 49% is smaller than 50%.

Teacher-independent activities

Choose from:

1   Give the children copies of Resource sheet 58 and ask them to complete the chart. They can use the cut-out cards from Resource sheet 57 to help them.

2   Let the children complete Resource sheet 59. They need to colour in a specific number of % squares using certain colours and then fill in a table to link the number of squares to fractions and percentages.

3   Use Resource sheet 10 to make a selection of fraction and percentage cards with fractions and percentages your children are familiar with, for example $\frac{1}{2}$, $\frac{1}{4}$, $\frac{1}{8}$, 10% and 50%. Let the children use them to play 'Fraction and percentage snap'.

4   Use Resource sheet 17 and fraction and percentage cards made from Resource sheet 10 and tell them to look for equivalences between fractions and percentages, for example $\frac{1}{2}$, $\frac{50}{100}$ and 50%. They should take it in turns to turn over the cards, and place them face up on a discard pile. Should the one they turn over match or be equivalent to the top one on the discard pile, they can move their counter one space along the track. The winner is the player who reaches the finish first.

Plenary session

- Discuss the successes of the lesson. What have the children learned? Brainstorm their answers.

- Go over the fraction and percentage equivalents and make a poster of these for a maths display.

- What did the children find difficult about the session? Note down on paper or on the board what they say, but also keep your own record of their thoughts.

Decimals in measure

Overall learning objectives

- Use decimal notation for tenths and hundredths.

- Understand the effect of dividing by 10 or 100.

- Know the relationships of familiar metric units.

- Represent length in decimal form.

- Represent weight in decimal form.

- Solve problems with measuring.

Key words

tenth	kilometre
hundredth	kilogram
metric	gram
centimetre	weight
metre	

Tenths and hundredths

Assessment focus

- Can the children use decimal notation for tenths and hundredths?

- Do the children understand what happens when they divide by 10 and 100?

Resources

- digits from 0 to 9 and a decimal point written on A4 card

- a set of digit cards for each child

- Resource sheets 17, 60, 61 and 65

- dice and counters

- cards with three-digit numbers written on them

- abacuses

- paper and pencils

With the whole class

- Tell the class that they are going to learn how to work with decimal numbers. Choose three digit cards, one of which should be 0. Give three children a card each and ask the others to order them to make the largest number. For example 2, 7 and 0 would be arranged as 720. Ask them what happens when the number is divided by 10. Aim for the answer *"It becomes 10 times smaller"*. Ask what the number will then become, in this case 72. Relate this to tenths and hundredths – dividing by 10 makes the number ten times smaller, by 100 makes the number one hundred times smaller. Repeat this using the same cards, but this time making the smallest number, noting how the 0 is not needed. Ask them what happens if you divide by 10.

- Select three new digit cards and the decimal point. Ask four children to take a card each. Tell the class to order them to make the largest number. For example 8, 1, 9 would be arranged as 981. Ask the three children holding the digits to each stand on the right of the child holding the decimal point (this will be on the left for the class facing them). Ask the class what happens when the number is divided by 10 and what it will become. Explain that the volunteers need to move one place to the right (as the class see it) to make 98.1. Discuss the position of the decimal point. Stress that it doesn't move, but rather the digits move right. Repeat this several times.

- Move on to dividing by 100 in the same way. For example 6, 8 and 2 would be arranged as 862 then divided by 100 to make 8.62; this time the digits move two places to the right.

With the lower-achievers

With adult support

Choose from:

1   Repeat the whole-class activity, asking the children to use their own digit cards and decimal point and relate this to an abacus. They should record their work on Resource sheet 60.

2 Use Resource sheet 61 to practise dividing by 10 and 10 and 10 and 10. Ask the children what is happening each time they divide by 10.

3 Use Resource sheet 17 as a game for at least two players. Fill in the sheet as shown below so that every other space on the track has ÷10 written in it and the others ÷100. The players need to have a game sheet each. You will need a dice, digit cards and counters. It is important for you to be there to ask the children what they are doing during their turn. To play, they take turns to throw the dice and move along the same number of spaces on the track as the number thrown. They then have to make a three-digit number using digit cards and divide

it by the number they land on. They should write the answer in or beside the space. The winner is the first player to complete the game sheet or the one with the most spaces filled in at the end of an agreed time limit.

Teacher-independent activities

Choose from:

1 Repeat the game using Resource sheet 17, after it has been played with adult support.

2 Use Resource sheet 60 (with a different picture from Resource sheet 65) for practice in dividing numbers by 10 and 100.

3 Devise a table of amounts of money for the children to fill in, involving dividing by 10 and 100.

Amount of money	÷ 10	÷ 100
£1.00		
£2.00		
£3.00		
£10.00		
£15.00		
£20.00		
£25.00		
£30.00		
£35.00		

Plenary session

■ Play a game similar to the one used in the whole-class session, using large digit cards and the decimal point card. Ask the children to help you, giving three of them a card each and a fourth the decimal point. Challenge the class to order the cards according to different criteria, for example nearest to 200, largest, smallest, nearest to 900; then divide by 100 or 10.

■ Assess the learning that has taken place by asking *"What happens when a number is divided by 10?"*, *"Does this always happen?"*, *"What happens when a number is divided by 100?"*, *"Does this always happen?"* and *"Who can write some numbers on the board and show us what happens?"*

- Hold up cards with three-digit numbers written on them, for example 456. Ask the children to jot down on paper what they would become if they were divided by 10/100. Give the lower-achievers one to do for every two or three that the others do. Select some of them to explain what has happened.

- Ask the children to make up numbers that you call out using their sets of digit cards and explain what each digit represents. For example in 249.6, the 2 is 200 and the 6 is 6 tenths of one unit; in 838.15, the 3 is 30 and the 5 is 5 hundredths of one unit.

Length

Assessment focus

- Do the children know the relationships between familiar units?

- Can the children represent length in decimal form?

- Can the children answer problems involving length?

Resources

- rulers and a metre stick
- digit cards
- Resource sheets 8, 62, 63, 64 and 65
- paper-clips
- two dice
- cm squared paper and pencils

With the whole class

- Ask the children to build numbers using digit cards and explain what each digit represents (see the last plenary session suggestion of the previous lesson). Link this to length by first talking about, and demonstrating using rulers and a metre stick, how many centimetres there are in a metre and how measurements that are whole metres and centimetres can be written. For example 1 whole metre and 50 centimetres can be written as 1.50m.

- Give each child a 'Show me' strip (Resource sheet 8) and a paper-clip. Call out some lengths for them to show on the strip. For example *"If one end of the strip is 1m and the other is 2m, put the paper-clip on 1.5m (1.2m, 1.25m, 1m 30cm and 1m 70cm)."*

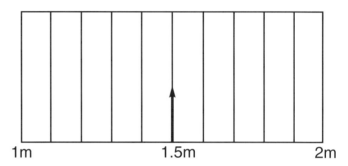

1m   1.5m   2m

With the lower-achievers

With adult support

Choose from:

1   Work with the children using the 'Show me' strips. Ask them to show you different lengths as in the introductory session above.

2   Ask the children to show you different lengths as above and then plot them on the strips on Resource sheet 62.

3   Practise dividing metre lengths by 10 three times. The children need to divide, for example, 10m by 10 to get 1m and then by 10 again to get 0.1m or 10cm and then again to get 0.01m or 1cm. They need to be encouraged to convert the single metre length into centimetres to divide by 10 and answer with both the m and the cm measurements.

4   Set them problems to do with drawing to a scale. For example, *"A table measures 1m by 50cm. Draw this to a scale of 10cm for every 1m."* You will need to explain to the children that the table is too big to be drawn on paper, so the size needs to be made smaller. It is easy to divide by 10 and make the size one tenth smaller. So they will draw the table to the size of 10cm by 5cm.

Teacher-independent activities

Choose from:

1 Give the children copies of Resource sheet 62 filled in as shown below (with a different picture from Resource sheet 65). Ask them to plot the measurements on the strips.

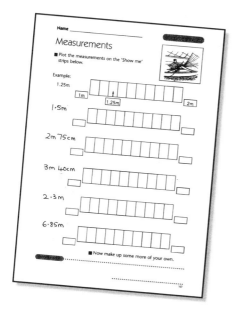

2 Use Resource sheet 63 for a paired investigation which requires the children to estimate length by finding an object similar in length to a decimal number they have made by throwing a pair of dice.

3 Ask the children to collect eight objects, measure their lengths in centimetres, then multiply these by 10 to convert them to millimetres and draw the length as accurately as possible on paper.

4 Use Resource sheet 64. An explanation will be needed before they can work on this sheet independently. Use the lengths on the sheet to make up a variety of addition and subtraction problems. These can be written, drawn or a combination of the two.

Plenary session

■ Write some lengths on the board and ask the children to tell you the other ways of writing them. For example, 250cm could be written 2m 50cm, $2\frac{1}{2}$m and 2.5m; and 1m 25cm could be written 1.25m, 125cm and $1\frac{1}{4}$m. Invite the lower-achievers to answer first.

■ The children could use their 'Show me' strips to show you different lengths, varying the measurements at the ends, for example sometimes between zero and 1 or zero and 2.

■ Ask the children what they have learned. Encourage the lower-achievers to answer first. Brainstorm their thoughts on the board.

> **We have learned...**
>
> I can write centimetres as decimals.
> $\frac{1}{2}$m is the same as 50cm.
> I can draw an object to a scale where 1cm represents 1m. This lets me make it small enough to draw.

■ Write some measurements on the board and invite the children to make up some problems using them. For example, you could write 1m, 50cm and 25cm, and they might say, *"I had 1m of string. I cut 50cm off to give to my friend and another 25cm to wrap a parcel. How much did I have left?"* Ask the rest of the class to answer them. This is a useful way of encouraging the children to think about the way problems are made up and what information is necessary to make it possible to answer them. Invite the lower-achievers to give some examples if they have worked on Resource sheet 63.

Weight

Assessment focus

- Do the children know the relationships between different units of weight?

- Can the children represent weights in decimal form?

- Can the children answer problems involving weight?

Resources

- Resource sheets 5, 8, 9, 10 and 62

- paper-clips

- grocery items such as tomato puree, cereal, a tin of baked beans, a bag of sugar or rice and a box of washing powder

- kitchen scales

- pens and paper

- balance scales

- number lines

- an assortment of classroom objects

With the whole class

- Remind the children about the work they did on length. Ask questions such as *"How many centimetres are there in a metre?"* and *"How else can we represent 1m 40cm?"*

- Ask them how many grams there are in a kilogram. Also pose the question how, using their knowledge of length, they can represent 1kg and 2000g (1000g and 2kg).

- Show the children a grocery item. Tell them what weight it is and ask them to estimate on their 'Show me' strips (Resource sheet 8) where the paper-clip would go to show the weight. For example, say *"This tomato puree tube weighs 270g. Your 'Show me' strip goes from 0 to 1kg, so whereabouts should the paper-clip be placed?"* Repeat this activity with other items, asking the children if they think the items will be heavier or lighter than the previous one by just looking. Invite a lower-achiever to weigh the items in their hands, doing a direct comparison, and say if they think their guess was correct or not.

With the lower-achievers

With adult support

Choose from:

1 Display the grocery packets on the table, with their weights concealed, with some calibrated scales and two large number lines. Ask the children to feel the objects and order them according to how heavy they think they are. Record this on one of the number lines. Ask them to check their estimates using the scales and then record this on the other number line, writing on the exact weights.

2 Call out weights for the children to mark on their 'Show me' strips using their paper-clips, for example 1.5kg, 1200g, 1kg 150g. Ask them to record their work on Resource sheet 62. You will need to write in the weights at each end of the strip, such as 1kg and 2kg.

Teacher-independent activities

Choose from:

1 Make further filled-in copies of Resource sheet 62. Include a range of weights, such as 2500gm, 3kg 400gm and 2.3kg. Again you will need to write in the weights at each end of the strip. The children mark these weights on the strips.

2 Collect five different items from around the classroom. Ask the children to pick them up and then order them according to how heavy they think they are. Write or draw this order on a number line.

lightest   heaviest

Weigh them using a set of balance scales and order them from lightest to heaviest. Draw or write this order on a second number line.

3 Repeat the activity using another five objects.

Plenary session

- Ask the children to use 'Show me' strips to show different weights that you call out. For example, *"If one end of the strip is 1kg and the other is 2kg, show me 1$\frac{1}{2}$ kg, 1500gm and 1.75kg."*

- Play a 'Ladders and snakes' game, using Resource sheet 9 and cards made from Resource sheet 10. Tell the children to mark the ladder with 0kg at the bottom and 7kg at the top. When you call out a weight, they should put it on their ladder. Any weights that will not fit should be placed on the snake. The winner is the child who fills their ladder first with the least number of weights in the snake. Play several games.

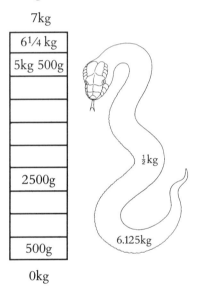

7kg

| 6¼ kg |
| 5kg 500g |
| |
| |
| |
| 2500g |
| |
| 500g |

0kg

½kg

6.125kg

- Play 'Bingo'. Ask the children to fill in the grid from Resource sheet 5 with kg and g weights, for example 3000g, 2kg 100g and 1kg. Ask them to keep within a limit, say 3kg. Call out weights, such as 3kg, 2.1kg and 1000g, and let the children cross them out if they have them on their grid. The winner is the child to cross all their numbers out first.

- Write some weights on the board, such as 2kg, 300g, 3$\frac{1}{2}$kg and 5000g. Ask the children to explain the other ways of writing the amounts and to tell you why, for example *"There are 1000g in a kg so 5kg must be the same as 5000g."*

- Invite the lower-achievers to explain the practical activities that they have been doing to the rest of the class.

Partitioning numbers

■ You will need these partitioning cards:

4, 5, 6, 7, 30, 50, 70, 90, 100, 200, 300 and 600.

■ Make up these numbers with your partitioning cards. How are they made up? Fill in the tables.

Number	Tens	Units
56	50	6
75		
37		
94		

Number	Hundreds	Tens	Units
156			
376			
695			
237			

■ Now make up some different numbers of your own to partition. Record them on the other side of this sheet.

Thousands

■ You will need these partitioning cards:

1000, 3000, 4000, 8000, 100, 200, 300, 600, 30, 50, 70, 90, 4, 5, 6 and 7.

■ Make up these numbers and partition them.

Number	Thousands	Hundreds	Tens	Units
4375				
8634				
3256				
1197				

■ Now make up some numbers of your own and partition them.

Number	Thousands	Hundreds	Tens	Units

Notes for adults •

Partitioning cards

1	2	3	4	5	6	7	8	9
10	20	30	40	50	60	70	80	90
100	200	300	400	500	600	700	800	900
1000	2000	3000	4000	5000	6000	7000	8000	9000

1	2	3	4	5	6	7	8	9
10	20	30	40	50	60	70	80	90
100	200	300	400	500	600	700	800	900
1000	2000	3000	4000	5000	6000	7000	8000	9000

Place value game

Player 1			Points	**Player 2**			Points
Hundreds	Tens	Units		Hundreds	Tens	Units	
		Total				**Total**	

Who won?

Notes for adults •••••••••••••••••••••••••••••••••••••••

Score 10 points every time you win.

Bingo!

Multiply by 10

■ Multiply these numbers by 10.
Put your answer in the empty row
under each number.

Thousands	Hundreds	Tens	Units
			6
			9
		8	7
		5	3
		9	4
	6	9	1
	8	4	2

■ What happens when you multiply a number by 10?

Divide by 10

■ Divide these numbers by 10.
  Fill in the empty rows.

Thousands	Hundreds	Tens	Units
		5	0
		3	0
	5	7	0
	9	7	0
8	6	9	0
7	0	0	0
3	8	4	0

■ What happens when you divide a number by 10?

Notes for adults ● Resource sheet 7 ● ● ● ●

Show me strips

■ Copy onto card and cut out.

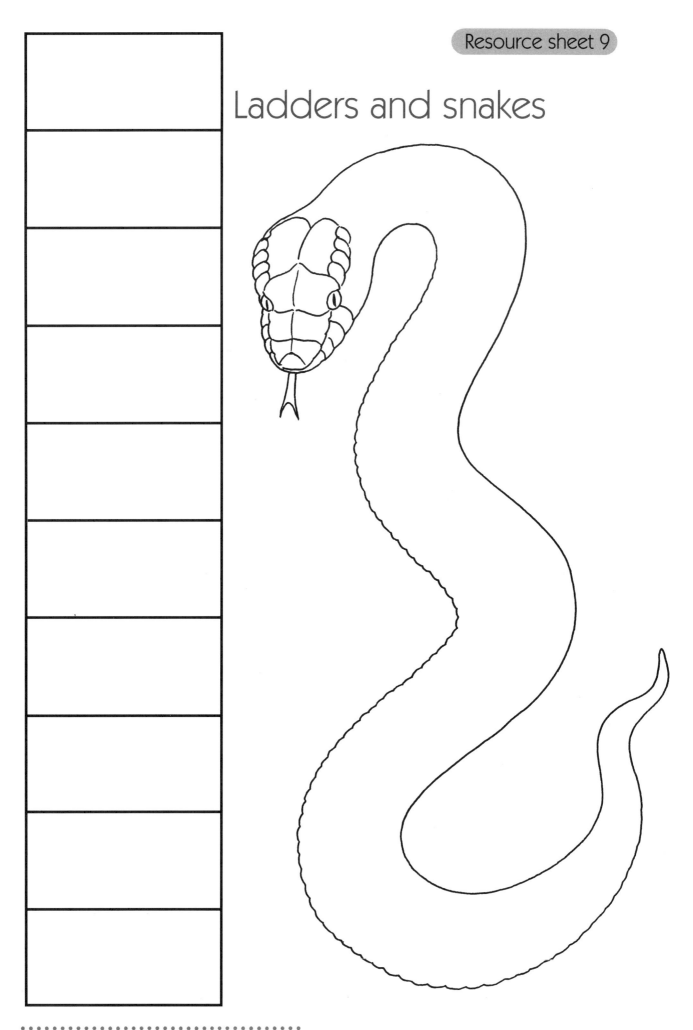

Ladders and snakes

Ladders and snakes

Blank cards

Name _____

In order

■ Put the numbers on the number lines in the right order.

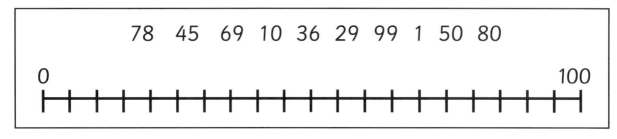

78   45   69   10   36   29   99   1   50   80

0   100

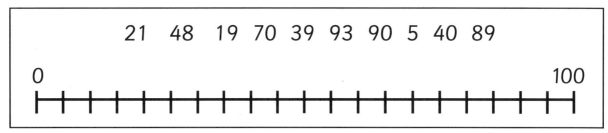

21   48   19   70   39   93   90   5   40   89

0   100

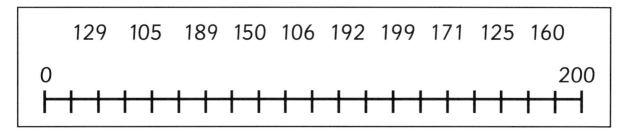

129   105   189   150   106   192   199   171   125   160

0   200

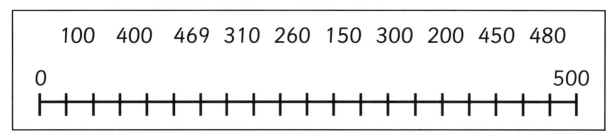

100   400   469   310   260   150   300   200   450   480

0   500

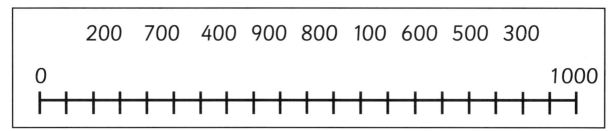

200   700   400   900   800   100   600   500   300

0   1000

Notes for adults ●

● ●

56

Name _____

Order decimals

■ Put the numbers on the number lines in the right order.

0.2   0.7   0.4   0.9   0.8   0.1   0.6   0.5   0.3

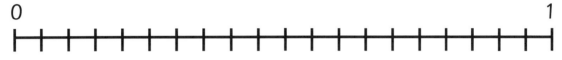

0   1

1.2   1.7   1.4   1.9   1.8   1.1   1.6   1.5   1.3

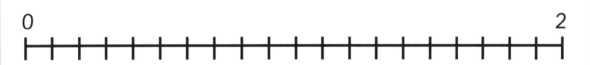

0   2

0.5   1.5   1.0   0.9   1.8   0.1   1.1   1.9   0.3

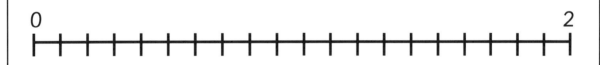

0   2

4.2   1.5   1.7   3.9   2.8   2.5   3.5   0.5   0.9

0   5

0.2   3.3   4.4   0.9   1.8   4.1   0.6   4.5   3.0

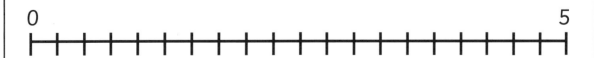

0   5

Number lines

-15 -14 -13 -12 -11 -10 -9 -8 -7 -6 -5 -4 -3 -2 -1 0 1 2
3 4 5 6 7 8 9 10 11 12 13 14 15

-15 -14 -13 -12 -11 -10 -9 -8 -7 -6 -5 -4 -3 -2 -1 0 1 2
3 4 5 6 7 8 9 10 11 12 13 14 15

-15 -14 -13 -12 -11 -10 -9 -8 -7 -6 -5 -4 -3 -2 -1 0 1 2
3 4 5 6 7 8 9 10 11 12 13 14 15

Thermometers

■ What temperatures are shown here?

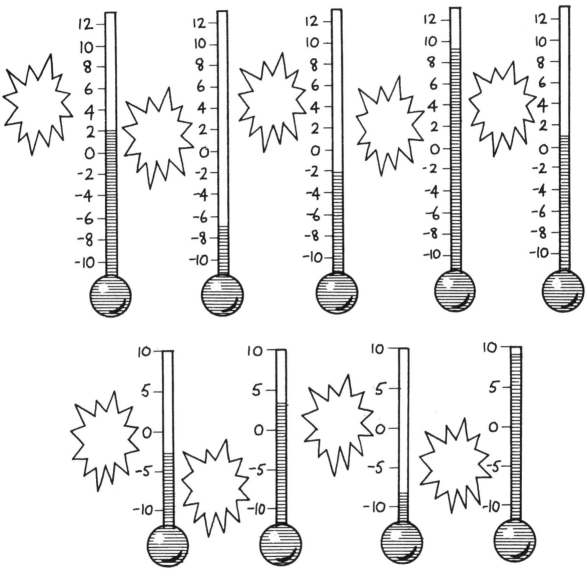

■ If the temperature rises by 2 degrees, what will the temperature read on each thermometer?

■ If the temperature drops by 2 degrees, what will the temperature read on each thermometer?

Notes for adults •

Where does it go? – 1

■ Plot the numbers on the number lines.

Example:

-4   3   9   13

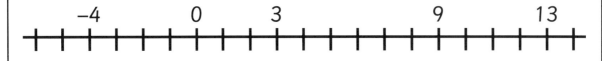

-5   6   11   14

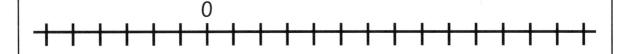

-6   -3   3   6

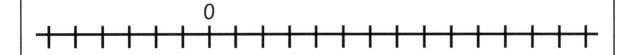

-3   -1   -2   13

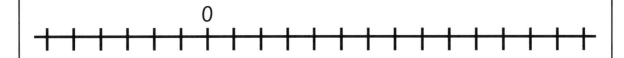

-6   -1   6   10

Now make up some for your friend to do.

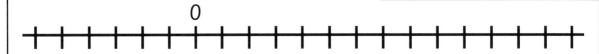

Notes for adults

Where does it go? – 2

■ In each box, put the numbers on the number line.

16   19   8   10   2

0   20

6   15   12   1   9

0   20

10   15   25   40   30

0   50

10   75   25   60   20

0   100

90   40   55   45   65

0   100

Track game

Where does it go? – 3

■ In each box, put the numbers on the number line.

Right or wrong?

■ Have a look at these calculations. Estimate whether each answer is correct. If it is, put a smiley face in the circle; if not, draw a sad one.

1. 78 + 34 = 102 ◯   5.   79 + 38 = 41 ◯

2. 64 − 29 = 35 ◯   6. 178 + 49 = 227 ◯

3. 93 − 57 = 46 ◯   7. 99 + 199 = 298 ◯

4. 22 + 91 = 203 ◯   8. 100 − 96 = 196 ◯

                        9. 138 + 66 = 298 ◯

■ Do the same with these problems.

1. Sam had £5. He bought a comic for 99 pence.
   How much did he have left? Answer – £5.99.
   Is that reasonable? ◯ Why? – Talk to an adult.

2. Sue was given £10 for her birthday. Her friend was given
   £25 for hers. How much more was her friend given?
   Answer – £25.
   Is that reasonable? ◯ Why? – Talk to an adult.

3. Bob had 59 marbles; his brother gave him another 32.
   How many did he have altogether? Answer – 91.
   Is that reasonable? ◯ Why? – Talk to an adult.

Notes for adults •

Talk about this sheet with the children. For example, ask *"How did you know that a calculation was wrong?"*

Estimate

■ Don't answer these calculations! Just estimate what you think they might be and put that answer in the cloud.

Example:

31 + 28

My estimate is ⟨ 60 ⟩ because

> 31 is close to 30 and so is 28. 30 plus 30 equals 60.

Try these:

My estimate is  because

My estimate is  because

My estimate is because

My estimate is because

My estimate is because

Problems

■ Solve these problems. Estimate the answer first
and then work out the answer and then check.
Work these out in your book.

Example:	The book cost £3.98. I gave £5 to the shopkeeper. How much change did he give me?	
My estimate is: Around £1 because £4.00 taken away from £5 is £1	My answer is: £1.02 because £4.00 taken away from £5 is £1 but I took away 2p too much so I must add it back on.	Have I checked my answer? Yes

1. I bought crisps for 43p and a drink for 79p. How much did I spend?

My estimate is:	My answer is:	Have I checked my answer?

2. Paul's T-shirt cost £6.99. He paid £10. How much change did he need?

My estimate is:	My answer is:	Have I checked my answer?

3. Sam bought 5 tins of cat food at 39p each. How much did he spend?

My estimate is:	My answer is:	Have I checked my answer?

Notes for adults •

Talk about this sheet with the children. For example, how did they know that
a calculation was wrong?

• •

Clock chart

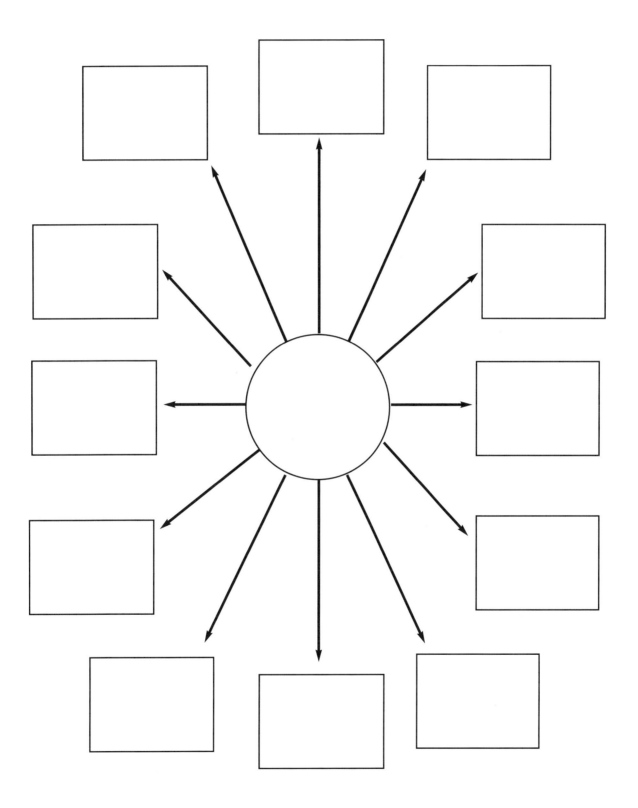

Flower chart

Flower

Split it up

■ Work out the missing numbers.
  Use the number lines to help you.

Example:

I know that 64 − ⟦ 22 ⟧ = 42 because 64 − ⟦ 42 ⟧ = 22

+18   +4

42   60   64   and 18 + 4 = 22

I know that

⌴_____⌴

I know that

⌴_____⌴

I know that

⌴_____⌴

I know that

⌴_____⌴

Notes for adults ●

Dominoes

47	21+21	42	29−12	17	35−30
5	15+6	21	20−8	12	20−5
15	30+5	35	44−14	30	50−30
20	15+34	49	35+30	65	15+16
31	12+29	41	6+17	23	25+11
36	25−11	14	38−11	27	32−28
4	42−40	2	14+11	25	26+21

Name _____

Count on or count back

■ Answer these by counting on or counting back. Check your answer by using the other method. Use the number lines to help you.

Example:

62 − 54 Answer = 8

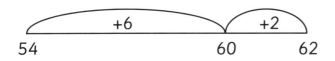

+6   +2

54   60   62

How did you find the answer?	How did you check?
Counting on	Counting back

	How did you find the answer?	How did you check?
68 − 35 Answer =	How did you find the answer?	How did you check?
49 − 38 Answer =	How did you find the answer?	How did you check?
76 − 61 Answer =	How did you find the answer?	How did you check?
83 − 59 Answer =	How did you find the answer?	How did you check?
100 − 76 Answer =	How did you find the answer?	How did you check?

Notes for adults •

Name _____

Round and rounds

■ Fill in the boxes to complete the loop.
Draw number lines to help you.

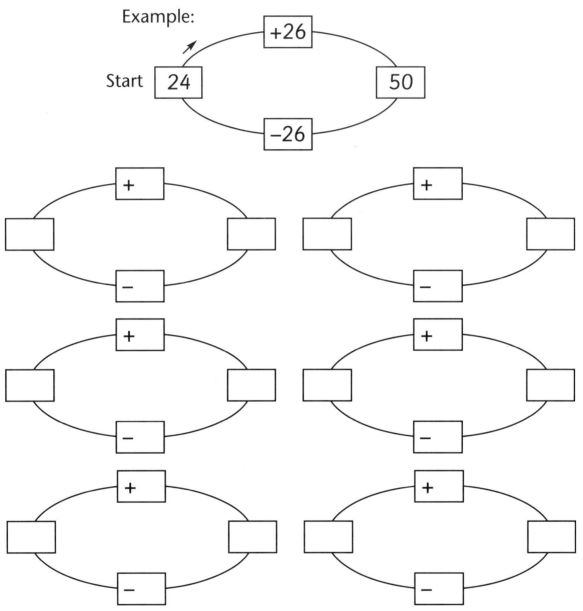

Example:

Start 24   +26   50   −26

Sam's problems

■ **Find the answers to Sam's problems by approximating first.**

Example:

Sam had 56 marbles. He was given 32 more. How many has he now?

Approximate answer = 90 (60 + 30 = 90)	Real answer = 88 (50 + 30 + 6 +2 = 88)	How close was your approximation? 2 over

Sam had 89p. He wanted £1.30 to buy a comic. How much more did he need?

Approximate answer =	Real answer =	How close was your approximation?

Sam had collected 125 football cards. His friend had 205. How many more did his friend have?

Approximate answer =	Real answer =	How close was your approximation?

Sam had 96 sweets. He gave his friend 52. How many did he have left?

Approximate answer =	Real answer =	How close was your approximation?

Sam bought 2 pizzas. The pepperoni one cost £2.50. The cheese one cost £1.99. How much did he spend?

Approximate answer =	Real answer =	How close was your approximation?

Sam had 36 red cars, 44 blue ones and 39 black ones. How many did he have altogether?

Approximate answer =	Real answer =	How close was your approximation?

Notes for adults ●

Name _____

Partitioning

■ Partition these numbers.

Example:

$45 = 40 + 5$	$228 = 200 + 20 + 8$
$38 =$	$253 =$
$27 =$	$256 =$
$39 =$	$138 =$
$56 =$	$124 =$
$73 =$	$237 =$
$91 =$	$562 =$
$84 =$	$348 =$

■ Now use your digit cards to make up some more two- and three-digit numbers to partition.

Number lines

Use the number lines to help you with these calculations.

Example:

$$58 + 61 = 50 + 60 + 8 + 1 = 110 + 9 = 119$$

```
        +60              +8   +1
 50              110    118  119
```

■ Now try these. The first one has been started for you.

1. $36 + 23 = 30 + 20 + 6 + 3 = \qquad =$

    ```
     30
    ```

2.

3.

4.

Name _____

Stepping stones game

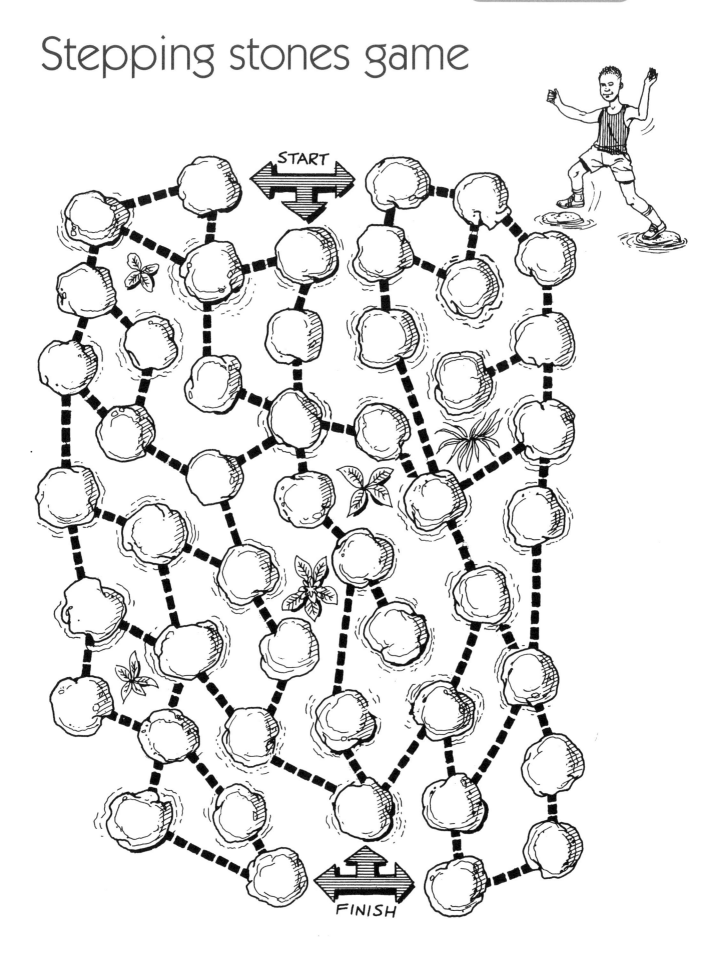

Back to zero

■ Start at 200 and race back to zero.
Throw two dice.

Turn	Player 1		Player 2	
	Score	Total	Score	Total
1	200 – ☐	= ☐	200 – ☐	= ☐
2				
3				
4				
5				
6				
7				
8				
9				
10				
11				
12				
13				
14				
15				

Notes for adults •

Children throw two dice, make a tens and units number and subtract that from 200.
They then carry that new number down to the next row in the column and throw again.

• •

Expanded subtraction

■ Do these calculations using the expanded method. Include negative numbers when you need to.

Example:

232 – 126
$$
\begin{array}{rrr}
200 & 30 & 2 \\
-100 & 20 & 6 \\
\hline
100 & 10 & -4
\end{array}
\qquad = 110 - 4 = 106
$$

1.

2.

3.

4.

5.

6.

Make your own subtractions

■ Use your digit cards to do this activity.

■ Make up some three-digit subtraction sums and
answer them using the expanded method.
One has been done to show you how.

Digits chosen	Subtraction calculation	Expanded method	Answer
3 4 6 1 2 7	463 −127	400　60　3 −100　20　7 ＿＿＿＿＿＿ 300　40　−4	340 − 4 = 336

Notes for adults •

This activity needs to be supervised.

Using known facts – 1

■ Use the multiplication facts given to make as many more facts as you can.

Example:

Because I know that 5 x 3 = 15, I also know that...
3 x 5 = 15   15 ÷ 3 = 5   15 ÷ 5 = 3   10 x 3 = 30
10 x 30 = 300   5 x 6 = 30   5 x $1\frac{1}{2}$ = $7\frac{1}{2}$ 10 x 6 = 60
10 x 12 = 120   5 x 30 = 150

Using known facts – 2

■ Use the multiplication facts to make new ones by multiplying by 10 and also partitioning.

Example:

6 x 4 = 24; therefore 60 x 4 = 240	
63 x 4 = 240 + 12 = 252	65 x 4 = 240 + 20 = 260
67 x 4 = 240 + 28 = 268	66 x 4 = 240 + 24 = 264
68 x 4 = 240 + 32 = 272	69 x 4 = 240 + 36 = 276

8 x 4 = 32; therefore 80 x 4 = ☐			80 x 40 = ☐				
83 x 4 = ☐	= ☐	85 x 4 = ☐	= ☐
88 x 4 = ☐	= ☐	86 x 4 = ☐	= ☐
87 x 4 = ☐	= ☐	89 x 4 = ☐	= ☐

9 x 4 = 36; therefore 90 x 4 = ☐			90 x 40 = ☐				
93 x 4 = ☐	= ☐	95 x 4 = ☐	= ☐
92 x 4 = ☐	= ☐	98 x 4 = ☐	= ☐
97 x 4 = ☐	= ☐	99 x 4 = ☐	= ☐

8 x 6 = 48; therefore 80 x 6 = ☐			80 x 60 = ☐				
83 x 6 = ☐	= ☐	85 x 6 = ☐	= ☐
88 x 6 = ☐	= ☐	82 x 6 = ☐	= ☐
87 x 6 = ☐	= ☐	89 x 6 = ☐	= ☐

6 x 6 = 36; therefore 60 x 6 = ☐			60 x 60 = ☐				
63 x 6 = ☐	= ☐	65 x 6 = ☐	= ☐
66 x 6 = ☐	= ☐	68 x 6 = ☐	= ☐
67 x 6 = ☐	= ☐	69 x 6 = ☐	= ☐

Notes for adults •

This needs adult support and discussion.

Facts challenge

Player 1's score

Player 2's score

· ·

Know your facts!

16	2 x 3	48	3 x 3	54	7 x 3
45	5 x 3	35	9 x 3	32	3 x 4
28	4 x 4	6	5 x 4	56	8 x 6
12	6 x 9	9	8 x 8	49	9 x 8
72	7 x 4	18	8 x 4	20	9 x 4
36	3 x 6	15	4 x 6	21	5 x 6
30	5 x 7	64	6 x 7	42	7 x 7
63	8 x 7	24	9 x 7	27	5 x 9

Adam's problems

■ Answer Adam's problems using grid multiplication.
The first one has been done for you.

1. Adam earned 65 pence for every book he sold.
   He sold 6 books. How much did he earn?

	60	5
6	360	30

   Answer = 390p or £3.90

2. Adam had 49 marbles. His friend also had 49
   marbles. How many did they have altogether?

3. Adam had 68 stamps in his small collection.
   His friend had 5 times as many.
   How many did his friend have?

4. Adam's school had a sponsored spell. He was
   sponsored 8p for every word he got right.
   He got 34 right. How much did he receive?

5. Adam wanted to get fit. He ran 23km every week.
   How far did he run over a period of 7 weeks?

Notes for adults • Resource sheet 39 • • • •

Multiplying with grids

Using a grid makes multiplying easier.

Example:

66 x 2

	60	6
2	120	12

= 132

1.

=

2.

=

3.

=

4.

=

5.

=

6.

=

7.

=

Notes for adults • Resource sheet 40

Yasmeen's problems

■ Make up some multiplication problems for Yasmeen to solve. Example:

| £24 x 3 | Yasmeen was saving for a CD player. She had £24 and she needed 3 times as much. How much did she need? |

| £10 x 5 | |

| £15 x 5 | |

| £8 x 7 | |

| 25cm x 4 | |

| 10cm x 3 | |

■ Now solve them!

Keep on halving

■ Divide these numbers by 2, 4 and 8 by halving.

Example:

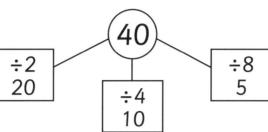

```
        ( 40 )
 ÷2       |      ÷8
 20     ÷4        5
        10
```

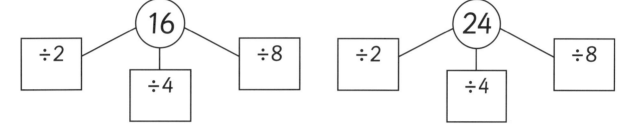

```
      ( 16 )              ( 24 )
 ÷2    |    ÷8        ÷2    |    ÷8
      ÷4                   ÷4
```

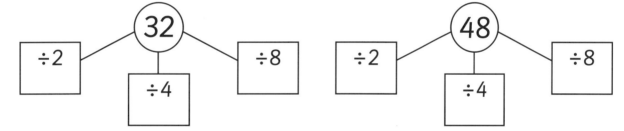

```
      ( 32 )              ( 48 )
 ÷2    |    ÷8        ÷2    |    ÷8
      ÷4                   ÷4
```

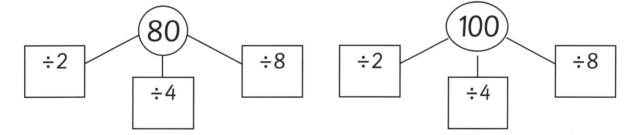

```
      ( 80 )              (100 )
 ÷2    |    ÷8        ÷2    |    ÷8
      ÷4                   ÷4
```

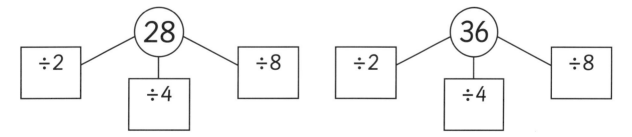

```
      ( 28 )              ( 36 )
 ÷2    |    ÷8        ÷2    |    ÷8
      ÷4                   ÷4
```

Notes for adults ●

● ●

Name _____

The factor challenge

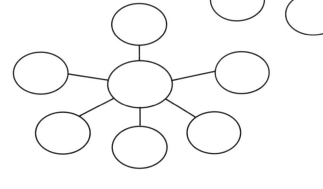

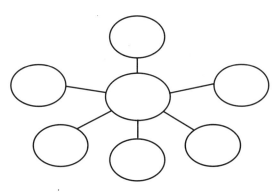

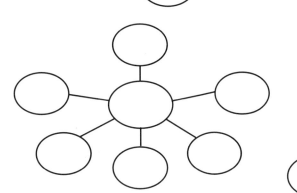

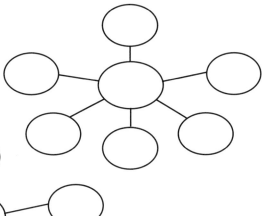

Name _____

a

Two answers

■ Find the two possible answers
for these calculations and
explain what you did.

Example:

3 x 4 + 5	It could be 17 if you multiply 3 and 4 and then add on 5. It could also be 27 if you add 4 and 5 first and then multiply by 3.

6 + 2 x 5

10 − 6 ÷ 2

15 + 6 ÷ 3

15 + 5 x 6

7 x 5 + 4

Using brackets

■ Put the brackets in the right place so that the calculations make sense.

Example:

$7 \times 5 + 2 = 49$	This should read $7 \times (5 + 2) = 49$

$6 + 4 \times 3 = 18$	This should read

$20 - 12 \times 3 = 24$	This should read

$15 + 9 \div 4 = 6$	This should read

$10 + 18 \div 2 = 14$	This should read

$32 - 6 + 2 = 24$	This should read

$5 \times 4 - 2 = 18$	This should read

$6 \times 3 - 10 = 8$	This should read

$20 + 20 \div 4 = 25$	This should read

$4 \times 9 + 3 = 39$	This should read

■ Now answer this problem and write a bracket number sentence to show what you did.

At the football tournament there were 10 five-a-side teams. Six children didn't turn up on the day. It was a shame but they played anyway. How many children played altogether?

Notes for adults •

The ski game

■ Help Martin down the ski slope.

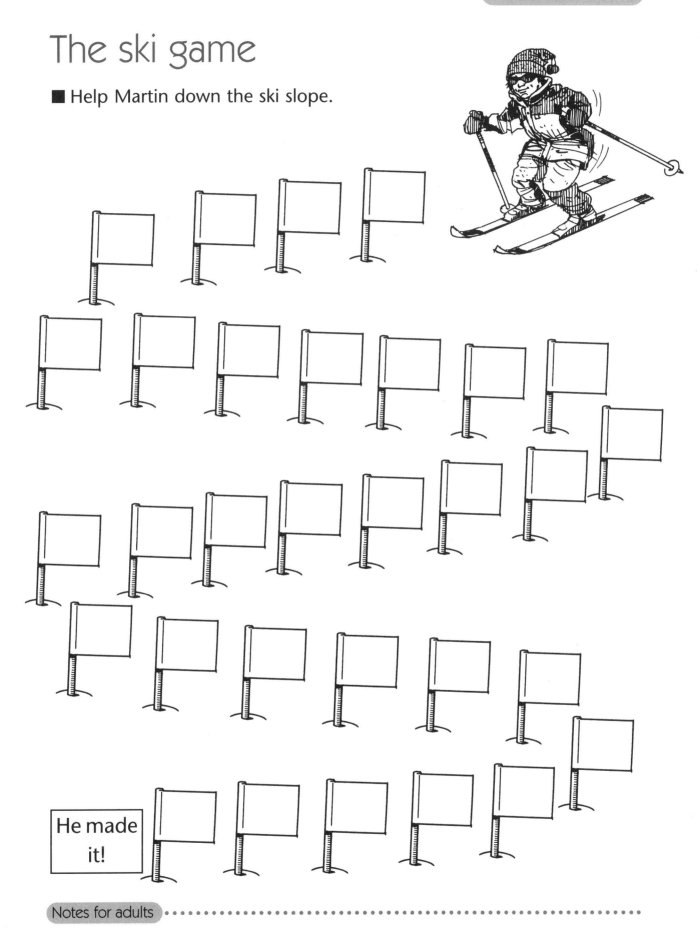

He made
it!

The grouping game

■ You need digit cards and different colour counters for each player.

5	4	3	5	8
9	6	2	7	10
10	12	4	4	9
3	8	6	12	5
7	11	6	8	2
2	5	4	10	11
9	3	11	7	7
8	6	2	12	3
4	10	11	8	9
12	7	5	9	6

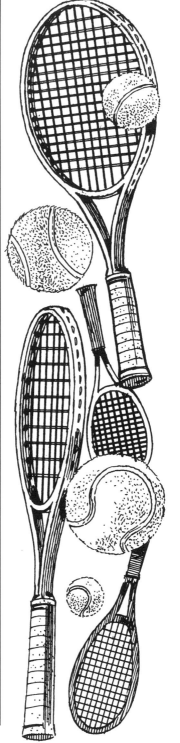

Notes for adults ●

Choose a divisor, for example 5. Make a two-digit number such as ☐2 ☐7 .
How many 5's in 27? 5 (and a remainder of 2). Cover a 5 with your colour counter.
The winner has the the the most squares covered.

Name _____

How many groups?

■ Work out how many groups of the divisor there are in these numbers. Write down your jottings.

Example:

| $72 \div 6 = 12$ | because 10 lots of 6 make 60, which leaves 12. 2 lots of 6 make 12. So, there are 12 groups of 6 in 72. |

<table>
<tr><td></td><td></td></tr>
<tr><td></td><td></td></tr>
<tr><td></td><td></td></tr>
<tr><td></td><td></td></tr>
</table>

What's left over?

■ Solve these calculations using grouping.
Make the remainder a fraction.

Jot your thoughts down on the sheet.

Example:

$34 \div 3 = 11\frac{1}{3}$

10 groups of 3 are 30, which leaves 4. Then one group of 3 is 3 which leaves 1. There are 11 groups of 3 and one left. The one is part of a group of 3 so it is $\frac{1}{3}$.

Use a tables square for support.

The leftover game

■ You need 40 counters and some digit cards.

Player 1

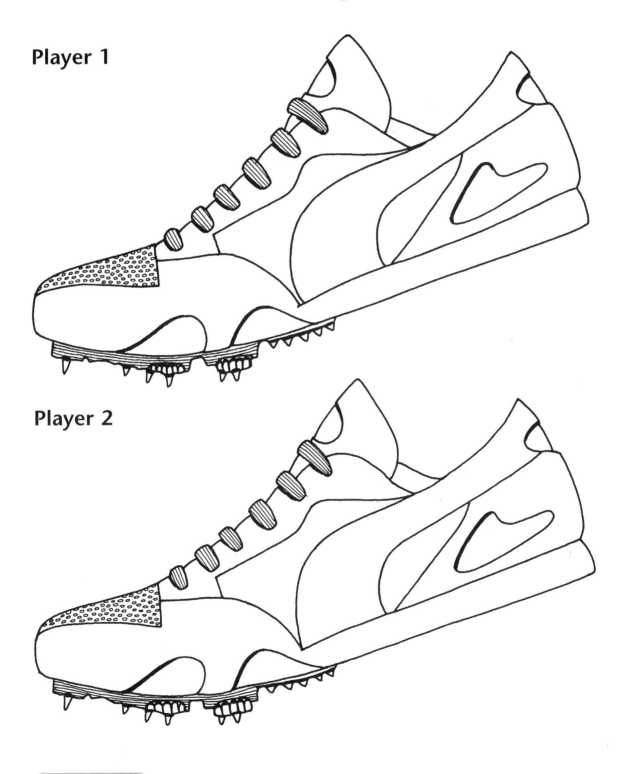

Player 2

Notes for adults ●

For two players. Choose a divisor such as 3. Use cards to make a two-digit number, for example ⬚2⬚ ⬚0⬚. 20 ÷ 3 is 6 remainder 2. Put 2 counters on your shoe. The winner has the most counters on their shoe.

Make a whole (eighths)

■ Pick a fraction card
and place counters on
the parts of your strip
that are equivalent to
the fraction. The
winner is the first
player to fill their strip.
If you can't use the
fraction card, you miss
your go.

Remember:

$$\frac{1}{2} = \frac{2}{4} = \frac{4}{8}$$

$$\frac{1}{4} = \frac{2}{8}$$

Player 1

Player 2

Fraction cards – 1

$\frac{1}{8}$	$\frac{1}{8}$	$\frac{1}{8}$	$\frac{1}{8}$
$\frac{1}{8}$	$\frac{3}{8}$	$\frac{3}{8}$	$\frac{3}{8}$
$\frac{3}{8}$	$\frac{5}{8}$	$\frac{5}{8}$	$\frac{1}{4}$
$\frac{1}{4}$	$\frac{1}{4}$	$\frac{1}{4}$	$\frac{1}{4}$
$\frac{3}{4}$	$\frac{3}{4}$	$\frac{1}{2}$	$\frac{1}{2}$

Make a whole (twelfths)

■ Turn over a fraction card. Place counters on your strip for that number of twelfths, for example $\frac{3}{8}$ is 3 twelfths. The winner is the player who fills their strip first.

Remember:

$$\frac{1}{2} = \frac{3}{6} = \frac{6}{12}$$

$$\frac{2}{3} = \frac{4}{6} = \frac{8}{12}$$

$$\frac{1}{6} = \frac{1}{12}$$

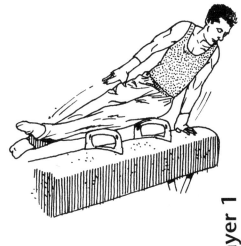

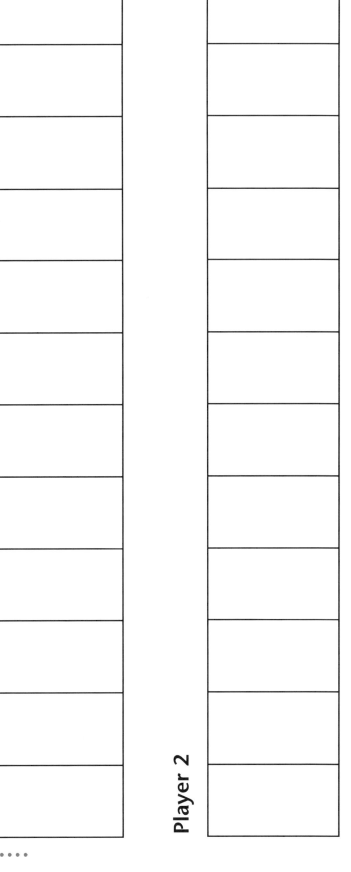

Player 1

Player 2

Fraction cards – 2

$\dfrac{1}{12}$	$\dfrac{1}{12}$	$\dfrac{1}{12}$	$\dfrac{1}{12}$	$\dfrac{1}{12}$
$\dfrac{1}{12}$	$\dfrac{1}{6}$	$\dfrac{1}{6}$	$\dfrac{1}{6}$	$\dfrac{1}{6}$
$\dfrac{2}{6}$	$\dfrac{2}{6}$	$\dfrac{2}{6}$	$\dfrac{3}{12}$	$\dfrac{3}{12}$
$\dfrac{3}{12}$	$\dfrac{5}{12}$	$\dfrac{5}{12}$	$\dfrac{7}{12}$	$\dfrac{5}{6}$
$\dfrac{1}{2}$	$\dfrac{1}{2}$	$\dfrac{1}{2}$	$\dfrac{2}{3}$	$\dfrac{2}{3}$

Name _____

How much is coloured?

■ How many whole strips and how many parts have been coloured?

Example:

= $2\frac{1}{4}$

2 whole strips and one part

=

=

=

=

=

=

=

=

=

Colour the fractions

■ Colour these shapes to show the improper fraction.

Example:

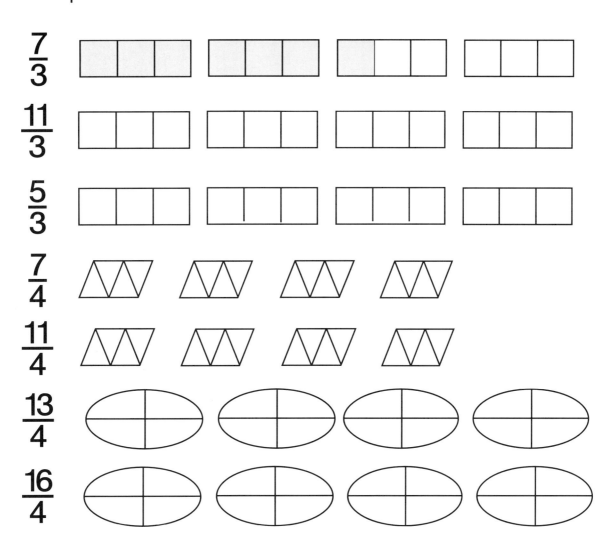

■ Now draw your own shapes.

$\dfrac{12}{5}$

$\dfrac{14}{5}$

Percentages

1%	1%	1%	1%	1%	1%	1%	1%	1%	1%
1%	1%	1%	1%	1%	1%	1%	1%	1%	1%
1%	1%	1%	1%	1%	1%	1%	1%	1%	1%
1%	1%	1%	1%	1%	1%	1%	1%	1%	1%
1%	1%	1%	1%	1%	1%	1%	1%	1%	1%
1%	1%	1%	1%	1%	1%	1%	1%	1%	1%
1%	1%	1%	1%	1%	1%	1%	1%	1%	1%
1%	1%	1%	1%	1%	1%	1%	1%	1%	1%
1%	1%	1%	1%	1%	1%	1%	1%	1%	1%
1%	1%	1%	1%	1%	1%	1%	1%	1%	1%

Snap!

■ As you match the fraction pieces to the percentages on the % square, fill in this table.

Percentage	Fraction (out of 100)	Fraction
50%		
	$\frac{25}{100}$	
		$\frac{1}{10}$
	$\frac{20}{100}$	
1%		
		$\frac{1}{20}$

■ Choose two other percentages and work out the fractions.

Coloured percentages

1%	1%	1%	1%	1%	1%	1%	1%	1%	1%
1%	1%	1%	1%	1%	1%	1%	1%	1%	1%
1%	1%	1%	1%	1%	1%	1%	1%	1%	1%
1%	1%	1%	1%	1%	1%	1%	1%	1%	1%
1%	1%	1%	1%	1%	1%	1%	1%	1%	1%
1%	1%	1%	1%	1%	1%	1%	1%	1%	1%
1%	1%	1%	1%	1%	1%	1%	1%	1%	1%
1%	1%	1%	1%	1%	1%	1%	1%	1%	1%
1%	1%	1%	1%	1%	1%	1%	1%	1%	1%
1%	1%	1%	1%	1%	1%	1%	1%	1%	1%

Colour: 25 squares red   1 square orange
          10 squares blue   5 squares yellow
          50 squares brown

Colour	Number of squares	Percentage	Fraction
Red			
Blue			
Brown			
Orange			
Yellow			

Divide by 10 and 100

■ Make some three-digit numbers using your digit cards and divide them by 10 and 100. Don't forget to use your decimal point. Record your answers.

Example:

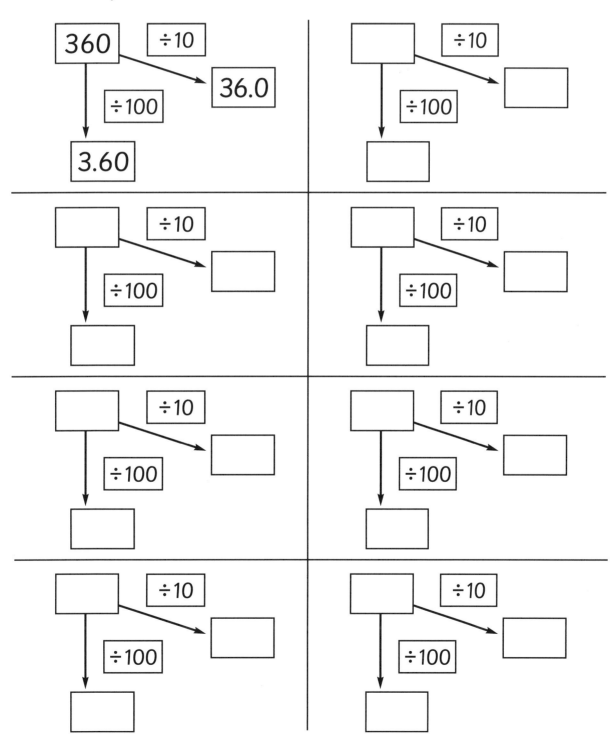

| 360 | ÷10 |
| 36.0 |
| ÷100 |
| 3.60 |

Divide by 10

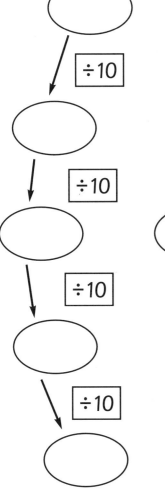

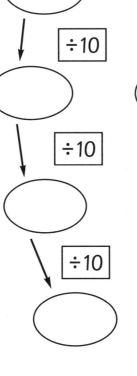

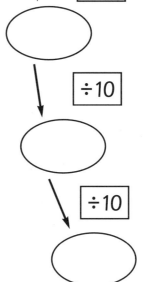

$\div 10$ $\div 10$ $\div 10$ $\div 10$

■ What happens when you divide by 10?

Name _____

Measurements

■ Plot the measurements on the 'Show me' strips below.

Example:

1.25m

| 1m | | | ↑ | | | | | | | 2m |

1.25m

■ Now make up some more of your own.

Notes for adults

107

Name _____

Paired investigation

■ Throw two dice, make a length out of the two numbers, and divide it by 10. Find an object that is similar to the length you have as an answer. Do this seven times.

Example: I threw a 5 and a 3

| 5 | 3 | ÷10 | 5.3cm | Pencil |

| | | ÷10 | cm | |

| | | ÷10 | cm | |

| | | ÷10 | cm | |

| | | ÷10 | cm | |

| | | ÷10 | cm | |

| | | ÷10 | cm | |

| | | ÷10 | cm | |

Notes for adults • Resource sheet 63

Measurement problems

■ Make up some addition and subtraction problems using these lengths.

Example:

1m	20cm	60cm
My sunflower was 1m tall. It grew 20cm one week and the next it grew another 60cm. How tall was it then?

1.5m	20cm	50cm

5m	2m	$\frac{1}{2}$m

2m	50cm	30cm

$1\frac{1}{2}$m	50cm	10cm

15cm	2cm	5mm

Now answer them!

Clip art

  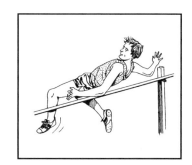

List of Assessment Focuses

Assessment focus	Chapter	Date achieved / comments
Can the children read large numbers accurately?	1	
Do the children know what each digit in a number represents?	1	
Can the children multiply and divide by 10?		
Can the children recognise and order negative numbers?	2	
Can the children calculate temperature rise and fall across zero?	2	
Can the children estimate the position of a number on a number line up to 100/1000?	3	
Can the children round numbers to the nearest 10/100/1000?	3	
Can the children use estimating to aid calculation?	3	
Can the children check to see if answers are reasonable?	3	
Do the children understand the relationship between addition and subtraction?	4	
Can the children check answers by using the inverse operation?	4	
Can the children partition numbers into H, T and U, adding the most significant digits first?	4	
Can the children make approximate answers?	4	
Can the children subtract 2 two-digit numbers mentally, using a number line for assistance?	5	
Do the children understand the use of approximation to assist their calculation of difference?	5	
Can the children build on their mental methods to develop their pencil and paper methods?	5	
Can the children use a variety of methods to multiply mentally?	6	
Can the children use a range of vocabulary for multiplication?	6	
Can the children use facts they already know to make up new ones?	6	

Assessment focus	Chapter	Date achieved / comments
Can the children recognise multiples of numbers up to 10?	6	
Can the children use pencil and paper methods to solve multiplication calculations?	6	
Do the children understand that division is the inverse of multiplication?	7	
Can the children understand and use the vocabulary related to multiplication and division?	7	
Can the children understand why brackets are needed?	7	
Can the children use a variety of methods for division?	8	
Can the children give the remainder in a quotient as a fraction?	8	
Can the children recognise equivalent fractions?	9	
Can the children compare and order fractions?	9	
Can the children begin to change improper fractions to mixed numbers?	9	
Can the children understand the relationship between fractions and percentages?	9	
Do the children understand that a % is a fraction of 100?	9	
Can the children use decimal notation for tenths and hundredths?	10	
Do the children understand what happens when they divide by 10 and 100?	10	
Do the children know the relationships between familiar units?	10	
Can the children represent length and weight in decimal form?	10	
Can the children answer problems involving length?	10	
Do the children know the relationships between different units of weight?	10	
Can the children represent weights in decimal form?	10	
Can the children answer problems involving weight?	10	